13 Horror

C000177151

Paul Groves and Nigel Grimshaw

Edward Arnold

a|io

© Paul Groves and Nigel Grimshaw 1978

First published 1978
by Edward Arnold (Publishers) Ltd
41 Bedford Square
London WC1B 3DQ

Reprinted 1979, 1981

ISBN: 0 7131 0300 0

Other books by Paul Groves and Nigel Grimshaw published by Edward Arnold:

Up Our Way	*13 Ghosts*
Living Our Way	*Monsters of Myth and Legend*
Going Our Way	*The Goodbodys*
Join the Action	*Smudge and Chewpen*
Action Replay	*13 Weird Tales*
Action Stations	*Smudge and Chewpen Tests*
Call to Action	

Text set in 12/14 pt. Photon Baskerville, printed by photolithography, and bound in Great Britain by Spottiswoode Ballantyne Ltd., Colchester and London

To the Teacher

This, like its two predecessors, *13 Ghosts* and *13 Weird Tales* contains a further thirteen tales of the horrific, written in simple English to put them within the grasp of the pupil who reads only occasionally or comes to reading with a certain degree of difficulty. Though we hope that each story has sufficient intrinsic interest to be read by the individual pupil for its own sake, each is accompanied by questions which point the way to written work or discussion. The first series of questions examines the reader's comprehension of the story and can usually be answered by reference to the text. The second set asks about the wider implications of the tale and refers to the pupil's own experience. Then there is a section on language generally, usage, meaning, and orthography. Finally come suggestions for written work ranging from the formal to the more imaginative.

Contents

Pet Food

... through the steady downpour was a hideous gobbling and worrying ...

Apart from the lights of his car, the world around was totally black. He was tired. It was raining. The car simply would not start. Repton closed the bonnet and went back to sit in the driver's seat. He was wet and cold but he would have to stay there all night. He switched off the lights to save the battery.

Then he switched them on again and shivered. The night pressed smotheringly on the windows. The thought of the wild, deserted country all round frightened him. He lit a cigarette and put it out almost at once. It was no good. He could not stay where he was. He felt more than uneasy, he felt tense, almost panicky. The night and the loneliness weighed on him threateningly.

He would walk back down the road. He had no sooner decided than he was out of the car, locking the door and walking away. He dimly remembered something lit by his headlights for a moment a couple of miles back. Had he seen a cottage or just an outcrop of rocks?

It was no better now that he was moving. He felt hunted and had to walk faster. He forced himself to slow down. In a moment he would have been running in blind panic as these nameless fears swallowed him up. There was nothing out there in the dark. He needed to hold on to that thought.

After the long day's drive, when he did see a light at last, he was too tired to hurry. But it changed things. Someone else was up and awake. He would find someone to talk to. Maybe he could get a hot drink, maybe even a bed to sleep in. He would be out of the wet. Panic was slowly leaving him.

He had to knock a long time at the door. The cottage seemed to hang above him, shapeless against the sky. Then the door opened and a weak light flooded the grass-grown path where he stood. The old woman stood, silent and un-moving, staring at him. As she held up the old-fashioned paraffin lamp he saw that her face was pale, wrinkled and dirty. Long grey hair hung over it. Only her eyes moved, flickering greedily over him from head to foot with the glint of beetles scurrying.

'Are you alone?' Her voice was harsh, unafraid. It had a rusty grate to it as though she seldom spoke.

'My name's Repton.' He cleared his throat to take away the slight quaver in his speech. 'My car—I was making for Laperham. My car broke down. It's back there on the road about a mile. Perhaps further. I am all alone. Have you a telephone?'

'A telephone?' She laughed, a gritty cackle. 'Not here. But—come in. You're all wet. Even a fine, sturdy body like you could take harm. Come in.'

The living room was directly behind the door. It was dim-ly lit. An old sofa, oozing stuffing, stood against the back wall. There were three chairs, broken and mended, a sideboard crowded with oddments, other stuff he could not see properly. The place was dusty and damp. It smelled of stale cooking and other things.

'Sit down,' she commanded. He slid off his raincoat, chose the strongest-looking chair and sank on it thankfully. 'Cup of tea?' she offered. She seemed sly to him and he told himself it was his imagination.

'Yes, please,' he said, and she poured it from a black teapot that stood on the hob. The cup was dirty but he took it gratefully. The tea, though, tasted bitter and he could not drink all of it.

'It's very good of you,' he thanked her. 'Er—how far is it to the nearest town—or any place where I could get some help with the car?'

'Too far tonight.' She shook her head. 'You'd walk miles. And—if you strayed from the road, you'd be in trouble. There are marshes here on the moor that could swallow a house. There'd be no one about to hear a cry for help.' She was watching him intently. The glitter in her eyes made him very uncomfortable.

'Do you live here alone?' He felt he had to say something.

'Not quite.' She cackled again. It sent a chill down his spine.

'Is there someone——?' The words died when he saw her smile. He was going to ask if there was someone she could send for help with the car.

'Not a someone.' She jerked her head towards the back of the house. 'It's outside.'

'Oh!' he said, disappointed. 'A sort of pet.'

'Yes. Sort of.' Again the laugh. He began to wonder if she was quite right in the head. He yawned suddenly and found his head drooping. He suddenly felt more than just tired.

'Come on.' She stood up. 'I can find you a bed. You'd like that, eh? Sleep here tonight? Go on tomorrow when you can see the way?'

'That's very kind of you.' He stood up, trying to shake off the strange tiredness and felt guilty. He had misjudged her. She was really quite kind.

'This way.' She picked up the lamp and climbed the steep stairs that ran up from one corner of the room. At the top was a very narrow landing and two doors ran off it. She opened one and led him in. There was a stump of candle in a saucer that stood on one of the two chairs. She lit it.

'You'll be all right here till morning. Put the candle out before you sleep.' She left him abruptly. He heard her clumping down the stairs. Then the house was silent.

There were no covers on the bed, only a stained old mattress. But he was too drugged with tiredness to care and he lay down. But, before he did so, something prompted him to jam a chair under the handle of the door. There was no lock.

3

His tenseness kept him from true sleep and he drowsed, fighting his way out of one bad dream after another. But it was not a dream that brought him sharply awake. The door creaked suddenly.

He sat up. It creaked again, as though a heavy sack had thumped against it. There was a kind of hoarse, snoring breathing there outside. His trembling hand, groping for matches, knocked the box on the floor. All sound outside the door stopped.

'Who's there?' His voice sounded stretched and high, even to himself. 'Is there anyone there?' he repeated and managed to get the candle lit. The chair still stood under the handle. Had it been pushed back a bit so that the door stood open a crack? Something went heavily down the stairs. He listened desperately.

Then, partly to his relief, he heard the mumble of the old woman's voice from below. There was a scrape and a rattle and then her voice again.

He grew brave enough to get off the bed. He went to the window and opened it, putting his head out. It was still pitch black and the rain was falling just as heavily as it had done before. He could just see the pale stripe of the road running away back towards where he had left the car. He went back to the door and put his ear to it. There was now no sound from below.

Slowly and cautiously, he pulled back the chair and opened the door. The landing was not quite dark. There was a glimmer of light from below. He put his head round the door.

Then he yelled, slamming the door, fumbling the chair back under the handle with trembling hands. The old woman had been standing at the foot of the stairs. She was holding an axe. But that had not been the full horror. It was the thing beside her, crouched, half in shadow, half-seen. It had snarled and gobbled at the sight of him before they had both begun their rush.

4

Whimpering, he was at the window and yelled again when he heard the door burst open behind him. Then he was out of the window, lowering himself to the full stretch of his arms.

But the old woman was in the room, standing above him, chopping down with the axe and at her side that other thing, slobbering. He caught a whiff of its breath, hot and eager. Then he fell heavily. He was in the road, running as fast as he could. He reached the car and fell against it. Sobbing, he managed to get inside and close all the doors. The windows were wound up tight.

He pressed the starter again and again until the battery died and the motor ceased to turn. Time passed and calmed him. There was nothing to be heard. Had he escaped? Was he safe?

Then he moaned, covering his face with his hands. Behind the streaming window swam the blur of the old woman's face. He could see the shine of her teeth, the grey hair flapping, as she peered at him. It was almost the last sound he could make.

She smashed in the windscreen with savage blows of the axe and the thing with her was on him, scrabbling through the broken glass for the door handle, opening it and tearing at him.

There was a high, choked scream. Then the only sound to be heard through the steady downpour was a hideous gobbling and worrying, like dogs on a fox or pigs at a trough.

The old woman stood, empty-handed, by the car. She had thrown the axe into the back. She went to wipe her hands on the grass verge. When she returned, she said smugly, 'I promised I'd get you another before Christmas, didn't I?'

She waited patiently, the shawl over her head. On her lips was the silly smile of a too-fond mother. At last she spoke again.

'Don't take all night,' she ordered. 'We've got to get what's left of him and this car deep under the marsh before dawn comes.'

Think it Over

What time of day was it? How do you know? Why was it so very dark?

Why did Repton switch off the lights? Why did he switch them on again?

Why did he walk back down the road?

When did his feeling of panic subside?

Why did he not hurry when he saw the light?

What did the old woman look like?

Why might she have had only a paraffin lamp?

What did the living room look like? What does 'oozing stuffing' mean?

Why would it have been dangerous to stray from the road on a dark night?

Why might the tea have tasted bitter?

What was it about the old woman that made him feel uncomfortable?

How was the bedroom lit?

Why did he jam the chair under the door handle?

What did he hear after the creaking door had wakened him?

Why could he not get a light at once?

Why did he yell when he opened the bedroom door?

What did he do when he got into the car?

How did the old woman get at him?

How did he die?

How does the old woman dispose of the car afterwards?

Do You Know?

Why does a car need a battery?

Does a cigarette really calm the nerves? Can you suggest other and better ways?

What is an outcrop of rocks?

How fast does the average man walk?

Why might Repton have been so tired? What sort of a job might he have had?

Why are some people afraid of the dark?

Why does the old woman ask Repton if he is alone?

Why does she laugh when he asks if she has a telephone?

What does a hot drink do to the body?

What or where is the loneliest house you have seen?

Why was there grass on the path of the old woman's house?

What is the untidiest room you have seen?

Where have you seen a marsh? What is dangerous about marshes?

How many stairs are there in your house?

How would you bar a door for which you had no key?

How would you escape from your bedroom, if you could not get out of the door?

What tells you that the downstairs rooms in the old woman's cottage are not very high?

How do you know that the thing had had other people to eat?

Using Words

What words could you use to describe a flat, deserted piece of country?

Bonnet. Write down ten other words which refer to a car. Check your dictionary to make sure you have spelt them correctly.

'My car broke down.' There are other expressions which use *break*. For example there are 'break up', 'break into', 'break out of'. Use these three in sentences of your own. How many others can you think of?

... 'sent a chill down his spine.' What other expressions, describing a feeling of fear connected with the body, are there?

List all the words ending '—ly' in the passage. Use five of them in sentences of your own.

Complete this sentence: 'Her greedy eyes looked like ...'

'He had no sooner decided than he was out of the car ...'
Complete the following sentences:
He had no sooner rung the bell than ...
He had no sooner left the house than ...
They had no sooner reached the beach than ...

Write out five questions that appear in the story.

Write Now

Describe the old woman's pet.

Describe how someone feels when he or she is running in a panic.

In play-form write out the conversation the old woman has with her pet when she tells it about Repton.

Have you ever been alone and out late at night in the country or a town? Describe what you saw and how you felt.

Write a pleasant story about an attractive pet OR write a poem called 'The Thing'.

Do you know about any unusual pets that people keep? Make a list.

The Tent of Mirrors

. . . she beckoned him with a twig-like finger . . .

Jim stopped running. He was far enough away now. His mother would not come after him, even if she knew he had got out of his room.

He had brought home a very bad school report. His mother had sent him to bed with no tea, to wait till his father got in and gave him the strap. He had tried to explain that what the teacher had called insolence was just fun, but she had not listened.

He was used to being sent to his room by his mother. That was not too bad. He was used lately to getting the strap as well. He could stand that. What was bad was that this was the first day of the mid-Lent fair. He had never missed that. That was why he had climbed down the drainpipe.

A man was just putting the gas lights on. He looked at Jim, as if he knew his secret. But now he could hear the sounds of the fair he did not care about the man, or his mother, or anything. He started to run again.

And suddenly there it all was: the big wheel, the helter skelter, the galloping horses. The excitement danced in his stomach. Then he remembered: he had no money. His mother normally gave him a half-crown for the mid-Lent fair.

Still, perhaps he would find some; he had once found a sovereign. He walked from one end to the other, his eyes fixed on the ground. But he found nothing.

He reached the far end by the bridge. He watched the barker at the boxing booth. 'Five pounds for anyone who can last three rounds with Battling Bert.' When he was older he might earn money that way but not tonight.

Next to the boxing booth was the tent of mirrors. And next to that, right at the end of the fair, was the freak show: real human freaks.

Sounds of laughter came from inside both tents. That was what he could do with, a good laugh. An old crone sat outside. She had no teeth. 'The laugh of a lifetime!' she spat out. 'The laugh of a lifetime!'

She looked at Jim for some time. Then she beckoned him with a twig-like finger. 'Do you want a laugh, boy?'

'Yes,' said Jim, 'but I've no money.'

She put her face close to his. 'Is your mother or father with you, then?' Her breath was hot.

'No,' said Jim. 'I've run off.'

'A fine boy like you should not be sad on a fair day. I'll let you in for nothing, if you clean a mirror for me.'

'Oh, yes, please,' said Jim.

'Come on then, boy. In you go and have a good laugh.'

He went in.

The first mirror made him look fat: his hips stuck out; his neck disappeared into his chest. He was just like a ball. He laughed.

The next was exactly the opposite. He was stretched out like a long piece of elastic. His legs were joined to each other. His arms looked like sticks. His head touched the top of the mirror.

He moved on to another mirror. In this one the top half of his body was normal but the bottom half was twisted like a genie coming out of a bottle. Tears rolled down his face, he was laughing so much.

Suddenly the twig-like finger touched him on the shoulder.

'Aren't you a funny sight? And me, too. What a fine pair we make!'

He could see them both now in the mirror. The old woman's body was joined to his. He could see her laughing, too. Her gums were black. Her mouth looked like a cave.

'Come on,' she said. 'I just want you to do this little job for an old woman. Then you can see the rest of the mirrors.' She led him under a flap in the tent. There was a large mirror covered in whitewash. She gave him a cloth. 'Just clean that like a new pin,' she said. Then she was gone.

This was an easy job. It was fun, too. He cleaned the top part first. Soon his head looked like a marrow with his ears stuck on the end like jug handles. He cleaned down the mirror. His body stretched out as well, like Humpty Dumpty. He was rolling with laughter. And his legs were like an elephant's. He polished the mirror weak with laughter; so weak he fell to the floor.

What was the matter? It was difficult to pick himself up. He could not pick himself up because his body was so heavy and his legs would not help him. He looked at them. They were thick like an elephant's. He touched them. Yes, they were his legs, he could feel them. He felt his body. He felt his head. Oh, no! HE HAD BECOME THE REFLECTION IN THE MIRROR!

A black curtain was suddenly flung over the mirror and the crone appeared from behind it. She cackled with laughter. 'What a fine freak you have become! What a lot of money you will be worth!' She fastened a chain round his neck.

She pulled him through into the next tent. It was the tent of freaks. There they all sat. Their empty, sad faces looked at him. He must escape. But his limbs would not do what he wanted them to do. He fell to the ground. The crone gave him a kick and left.

Soon people came in to look at him and his companions. He tried to tell them about the old lady but only dribble came out of his mouth. They pointed at him and laughed.

He cried. His face was one mass of wetness. A small boy threw a stone at him and ran out.

As the evening wore on, more and more people came in to see the freaks. Many were drunk and poked them with sticks. He kept trying to tell them who he was but no words came, only the dribble.

But then it was going to be all right. His sister and her boy friend came into the tent. They had obviously come to rescue him and take him home. He put out his heavy arms to her. But she screamed. "Keep him away from me!' The boy friend beat him to the ground with a stick. She ran out of the tent. Her boy friend followed with a curse.

She had not known him. Would any of his family know him ever again? Was he to be like this always?

The weeks went by. The fair was touring round the country. He knew this because he kept being pushed into a caravan which moved. The people, too, who came to see him, would speak in different dialects. He lived in the caravan with the two other freaks. One of them was called Satan by the old woman because he was the ugliest of them all. When the old lady was not there he kept making signs to Jim. He seemed to be rubbing something and pointing in the direction she had gone.

Gradually, and all things came into his mind gradually these days, he came to know what Satan meant. They must get revenge. If they were to be freaks, the old woman must be as well. They must get her in front of her own mirror. He made a sign to Satan to show that he had understood. The look in Satan's eyes showed that the message was known to him.

Their chance came a few days later. The fair was setting up in a new town. The old crone had put the keys to the chains on the table as she fed Satan. He suddenly fell against her, putting all his weight on top of her. The wind was knocked out of her so that she could not scream at first and when she could, her voice was drowned by the sound of the steam organ being tested. Jim had slightly better control of his hands now and after ten minutes he got the key in the lock and released Satan. Then he released himself, as Satan held the old woman on the floor; and then the other freak. Now, could they get her to the mirror before they were discovered?

It took them a quarter of an hour but they did it. They pushed her right up against it and held her there with their bodies while they groped to pull the cloth off with their fumbling hands.

It fell to the ground. She gave a scream which slowly became a gurgle in the throat, as she changed into a freak. Jim wanted to laugh and point at her like the people did who came into the tent, but he just stood there swaying on his heavy legs.

But the legs became lighter. His arms became controlled. His dribbling stopped. He noticed Satan was shrinking in size. He shrieked with joy, for he could now make a proper sound again. Satan was like a normal boy. He looked down. He was like a normal boy again, too. The other freak was a small red-headed girl. They all hugged each other in joy.

They chained the old woman up in her freak tent. But she was cold. The shock of the change had killed her. They watched her body slowly change back. Jim and Satan were afraid their story would not be believed so they ran away to sea. They never left each other's side and this story would not be known if Jim's diary had not been found in an old sea chest.

We do not know what happened to the mirror. Beware next time you are at the fun-fair.

Think It Over

Why had Jim been sent to bed with no tea?

How do you know his father was a strict disciplinarian?

Why had Jim disliked being sent to bed this time more than ever before?

How do you know he was excited by the prospect of the fair?

How did Jim usually get money to spend at the fair?

Name two ways in which Jim thought he might get money.

Where was the tent of mirrors? What was next to it?

Why did the mirror need cleaning?

What happened when Jim had finished cleaning the mirror?

When do you first suspect that the old crone is a witch?

Why was it difficult for him to walk?

Why could Jim not talk to other freaks or people as they came in?

What happened to Jim when he reached out for his sister?

Who did Jim manage to communicate with in the end?

What did they decide to do?

What happened to Jim and the other two freaks, when the old crone was changed by the mirror?

Why had the old crone died?

Why did Jim and Satan run away to sea?

Why should you be careful next time you go to a fun-fair?

Do You Know?

What is Lent? What are the other two main Christian festivals of the year?

Why is it dangerous to climb down a drainpipe?

How do you know this is not a modern story? Give at least three reasons.

What is a sovereign worth today?

How do you earn money at a boxing booth?

What is a freak?

Why does the old crone ask whether Jim has his mother or father with him?

What is a genie? Where would you find stories about genies in bottles? In what book particularly?
Why did the old crone fling a black curtain over the mirror?
Why was the freak with Jim called Satan? Who is Satan?
How do you know Satan is very large and heavy?
What is a sea chest? Are sea chests still used today?
   What would a sailor have nowadays?

Using Words

What is the best comment you have had on a school report? What was the worst? Was it fair?
What is another word for *insolence*?
What is a fairground barker? Why is he so called?
What is a helter skelter?
Use *too* twice in the same sentence of your own.
Write a sentence that begins with 'What' which is not a question.
Use the colon to introduce a list of things you would find at a fair, e.g. At the fair you would find: . . .
'The excitement danced in his stomach.' Write this another way.
A 'round' is a period of time. How many other words can you think of connected with sport which mean a period of time?
'I've run off.' How many other expressions are there which use *run,* e.g. 'run into', 'run out of'. Use these two and any others you can think of.
Write out all the sentences in this story in which the word *like* appears.
'She cackled with laughter.' What kind of animal was she like? How many other words can you think of which describe the sounds animals make?
What is dialect? What dialect words are used in your part of the country?

'If they were to be freaks, the old woman must be as well.'
Write two sentences of your own beginning 'If . . .'

'Satan's eyes.' Which of these should have an apostrophe:
apples and pears; says; Jims house; dogs collar?

'bel*ie*ved' Write down three more words with *ie* in them and
two with *ei*.

Use each of these words in a sentence of your own: excitement, reflection, mirror, fastened.

Write Now

You break a mirror one morning. What happens that day?

You tour the country with a fair. Describe a day in your life.

Write a story about an old-fashioned boxing booth.

How did the small red-headed girl come to be in the old
crone's power? Write her story.

List all the nursery-rhyme characters you can remember.

In play-form write the conversation Jim and Satan have
when they discover the old crone is dead.

Write a poem called: 'Trapped' or 'Changes'.

Jim revisits the town as an old sailor. What does he think
about as he walks round?

Lovers' Quarrel

. . . blood began to well up from the thin red line across her palm . . .

Della shivered suddenly and wondered why. Peter's dressing room was warm enough. He would be with her in a moment. He was the star of the show. His ventriloquist's act was top of the bill. And he was taking her out. Why should she feel worried and uneasy?

There were two chairs in the room. On one lay a book. Peter's doll, Madame Belle, lay sprawled on the other. For a moment, Della looked at the flowing, pink dress, the long, blonde curls, the silver shoes. Her eyes flicked to the painted face with its wide, red mouth, the too bright cheeks and the strangely living eyes. Shivering again, she looked away and picked up the book. There were photographs and newspaper cuttings in it. She turned the pages until one picture took her interest. It was of a very pretty girl. Then she heard footsteps outside and the door opened.

'Peter!' Her face lit up.

'Darling!' He kissed her. 'Sorry I kept you. I got talking. Ready to go?'

'Oh yes. But—who's this?' She showed him the picture. He glanced at it and his face changed.

'A girl called Moira Marsh,' he told her almost roughly.

'Were you in love with her?'

'Perhaps.'

'What happened?' Della asked.

He looked at her, his eyes dark and his mouth a thin line. 'She was murdered.'

'Murdered!' She dropped the book hurriedly back on the chair.

'Stabbed to death. Her face——. Her tongue——' He

17

shook his head. 'I don't want to talk about it.'

'And the murderer?' She stopped.

'They never found him.' Peter reached for his coat. 'Let's not talk about it now, eh?'

'No. Poor you. Poor girl.' She took his arm and gave a last glance back at the dressing room as they left. It seemed more dismal than ever now. The doll lay sprawled out in that chair like a corpse.

But then they were out for dinner and she forgot all about poor Moira Marsh. It was a wonderful evening. She was more than half in love with Peter. Did he feel the same about her? He certainly behaved as if he did.

She was a dancer in the chorus. Normally she would not have been asked out by a star like Peter. He had travelled all over Europe and America with his act and it had made him famous. It was an unusual sort of act because the doll was a woman. It was funny to watch but it was more than that. Peter and Madame Belle together were like a mother and son, a husband and wife, a man and his girl friend. They were so good that, at times, you forgot that Madame Belle was only a doll. There was something extra about the act, almost magical.

But Della did not love Peter just because he was famous. He was handsome. And there was more than that. He had moments of quiet when he seemed sad and troubled. There were depths to him.

The next night he had asked Della to go out with him again. Della went round to his dressing room after the show and stopped, frowning, outside his door. Peter was talking to another woman. She sounded angry.

'—see her again,' she said.

'This time—' Peter sounded almost pleading but he was not allowed to finish.

'You know what will happen,' the woman insisted.

'No!' Peter cried.

Della laughed suddenly and knocked on the door. She

had recognised the voice. It was Madame Belle's. After a moment or two, Peter opened the door and let her in. They had another splendid evening together.

Then the blow fell. She could hardly believe it. Peter told her he did not want to see her again. He was not finishing his contract at the theatre. He would end the week and he would go. He told her in short, cold phrases. He did not even look at her. She could find nothing to say until he turned to go.

'Peter!' she said.

'It's no use, Della.' He still did not look at her. 'It's all over.'

'But it can't be!' She was starting to cry. 'You can't just leave me like this. I love you. I thought you loved me.'

'You were wrong,' he said harshly and left her. She was too upset to follow him then. She could hardly get through her dances in the chorus.

But, when the show was over, she felt able to go and see him. There was no answer when she knocked on the dressing room door. She went in. The place was empty except for the doll, Madame Belle. Those glassy eyes seemed to stare at her and the wide, empty smile on the wooden face seemed to sneer. Della walked about the room nervously. The theatre was very quiet. She heard voices call as the last people went home. She prayed that Peter had not gone, too. She would have to tell the stage-doorkeeper she was still here. Otherwise she might get locked in. But she would wait a moment.

Idly she picked up the book of photographs and clippings and looked through it. There were photographs of people with whom Peter had been in shows, reviews of the act. There was the photograph again of the murdered Moira Marsh. She turned pages quickly. Then she stopped. The newspaper clipping that had caught her eye was different from the rest. It was from an American newspaper. 'Savage Murder' the headline ran. She read the rest of the print. The body of a young woman had been found on a piece of waste ground. The girl had been stabbed many times. Her face had been so badly slashed that she could not be recognised. There were other details. Della closed her eyes. She felt slightly sick.

'Put that down!' It was a woman's voice, sharp and vicious. Della gasped, dropping the book. There was no one in the room except for herself and the doll. The utter silence in the rest of the theatre was terrifying. Shaking, she moved towards the door and gasped again as it opened. When Peter came in, she tried to cling to him but he pushed her away.

'She knows about us,' the strange voice accused. Della looked at him and back at the doll. It seemed to have moved.

'Peter!' she whispered and then, more strongly, 'Peter! Stop it! It's you, throwing your voice, isn't it? It was you, outside the door, just now, wasn't it? Please stop. You're frightening me.'

He stared at her with a face like stone.

'I told you what I would have to do,' the cold voice rattled on. 'If we let her go, give her time to think now, she'll realise about the murders.'

'Murders?' Della breathed. She looked at the doll. Surely it had not been sitting up before!

'Moira Marsh,' Madame Belle clacked. 'And the girl in America. You've seen the photograph. You know that story. You've seen the newspaper cutting. You would have realised sooner or later.'

'Murder, Peter?' Della's shaking hand fell away from his arm. 'Both of those girls?'

But he hardly seemed to hear her. He was gazing at the doll. As if sleepwalking, he turned the key in the lock of the door and dropped it in his pocket.

'That's right,' Madame Belle approved. 'I told you how it would have to be, didn't I?'

He was by the dressing table and he opened a drawer. Della could not move. The snake-like stare of the doll's eyes held her to the spot.

'You little fool!' Madame Belle hissed. 'Thought you could have him, did you? Thought you could take him away from me? Like the others. You know what happened to them.'

'Peter!' Della said. But he was silent, looking down into the drawer.

'He's mine!' the doll croaked. 'He belongs to me. No one else can have him. That first girl in America. She thought she could take him away. But I showed her. I showed her different. Didn't I, Peter?'

He nodded his head once like a puppet.

'And Moira Marsh. You tried to cheat me, didn't you, Peter? You said there was nothing between you. But I knew better, didn't I?'

He nodded once more like a machine.

'And now, you!' Madame Belle spat, the wooden mouth rattling. 'You thought you were very clever. Thought you could steal him from me. So sweet and loving. Well, you'll see. Peter!'

'Oh, God!' Della backed away from him. Her legs felt so weak that they could hardly carry her. His blank eyes stared unseeingly at her. There was a knife in his hand. As he advanced, she screamed.

'Kill her, Peter!' the wooden voice ordered. 'Kill her now. Stop her noise.'

Peter came at her silently. Somehow she managed to avoid him but there was a sharp pain in her hand. Blood began to well up from the red line across her palm. As he came at her again, the head of the doll turned of its own accord to watch. Della screamed, grasping desperately for something to defend herself with. Her shaking fingers closed on the legs of the doll. They seemed to writhe under her touch. Hardly knowing what she was doing, she swung the body. There was an angry cry and a groan. The doll had cried and groaned as her wooden head had struck Peter's. Stunned for a second, he dropped the knife. Della fumbled on the carpet and picked it up.

Madame Belle lay twistedly on the floor. Her limbs seemed to move as if she were getting to her feet. 'Kill her!' she was croaking. 'Kill her, Peter!'

He rushed at Della and blindly she tried to push him away. The colour left his face and he staggered back. The handle of the knife stuck out between the fingers he held across his chest. He slumped back into a chair, the front of his shirt bright red. But it was the doll on the floor that was moaning weakly.

When the doorkeeper, alarmed by the noise, broke down the door at last, he found Della crouched in a corner with her hands over her head. It was thought that the murder was the result of a lovers' quarrel. Della never recovered enough to tell them differently.

In the place where she is now kept for the rest of her life, she is very quiet. But she has been violent at times. They do not now let her see any variety acts on television. They upset her too much, especially puppets or ventriloquist acts.

When the doorkeeper came in, he found the doll shattered and broken. In her terror and madness, Della had smashed it over the back of the chair. Its limbs were scattered across the room. It was all part of the horror for him. He could not forget it. Whenever he told the story, he would mention it.

'She'd knocked the doll's head clean off,' he would say. 'She was crouched there in the corner and it was right next to her. One of its eyes was gone. But, with that wooden mouth open, it looked for all the world as if it was trying to bite her.'

Think It Over

Where does the story take place?

What kind of an act did Peter have?

What was particularly frightening about the doll's face, when Della first looked at it?

What else did Della look at as she waited for Peter?

Who was Moira Marsh? How did she die?

How did Della feel about Peter?

What part did she play in the show?

What did Peter tell Della that upset her very much?

What frightened Della when she was alone for the second time in Peter's dressing room?

What did the doll tell her about the murders?

Why could Della not escape from the room?

Does Peter really want to murder Della?

How did Della defend herself?

How was Della's life saved?

What was the general opinion about Peter's death?

Where did Della spend the rest of her life?

What did she particularly dislike seeing on television?

What did the stage-doorkeeper say about the doll's head?

Do You Know?

What is a ventriloquist? Can you name some ventriloquists? What is your favourite ventriloquist's dummy?

What does a stage-doorkeeper do? What is a dressing room?

What letters are difficult to say without moving your lips?

What was different about Peter's ventriloquist act? Who operated the doll and made it talk?

Why does a snake seem to stare?

Mention two ways in which a puppet can be worked.

Why does the colour leave a sick person's face?

Name an American paper.

Why do actors and entertainers keep books of newspaper cuttings? Have you ever kept a scrap book? What sort of things did you put in it?

Did you find anything particularly horrifying about the doll? What was it?

Using Words

'top of the bill.' What is the meaning of the word *bill* here? How many other meanings of the word can you find? Can you use each correctly in a sentence?

Note how this sentence is punctuated: 'Peter's doll, Madame Belle, lay sprawled on the other.' Now punctuate these sentences:

Williams the full-back was brought down from behind.

Della a member of the chorus was found guilty of murder.

List some of the clothes you are wearing. Make sure you punctuate the list correctly.

'a very pretty girl.' How would you say this if you were talking to a close friend?

'Sorry I kept you.' Write down another way of saying this.

" '—see her again,' she said." What would the complete sentence have been in the story?

'Then the blow fell.' Write this in another way.

" 'Moira Marsh,' Madame Belle clacked." Why is the word *clacked* used here?

'But he hardly seemed to hear her.' Use the word *hardly* in a sentence of your own.

What kind of animals writhe?

What are limbs? Do only human beings have them? What does 'out on a limb' mean?

Complete the following:

America   —   American

France   —
Holland   —
Denmark   —
Venice   —
'Vicious', list two more words ending -cious.

Write Now

Make a list of all the theatres you know.

Write a story about a girl and her doll or about a ventriloquist and his dummy. It need not be a horror story.

How had Peter's doll, Madame Belle, come to have a life of her own? Make up your own explanation.

In play-form write down what the stage-doorkeeper told the police.

The Picture

. . . Long, pale and bony they reached out for him . . .

Jim Dodds was a clever man. He thought so. He would visit old people in out-of-the-way places and buy what they had to sell. Old silver, old gold, old pictures, old furniture. They did not know the value of such things. Jim did. And he was a good talker. He made a good living.

Some people would have said that Jim was a cheat, or worse. Jim would not have minded that. In this life, for good or evil, you take your chances. That was how Jim felt.

He would come across some old woman. She would have an old plate or an old teapot or an old chair.

'What do you want with that, granny?' Jim would ask. 'Taking up space. Gathering dust. It's not worth much but I might find a use for it. What do you say? Give you a pound for it.' He would tell them that their silver was pewter, that their chairs were worm eaten. They would be grateful to him for taking things away. Later, he would sell the stuff for many times what he had paid for it. The chair that had looked so old and worthless in the old lady's dark little cottage would sell for a hundred pounds in London.

Of course, he never went back to the same place twice. Not if he could help it. Someone, in the meantime, might have told the old lady what her stuff was worth.

Why, then, did he go back to the village of Markell? On his return he only visited one house. And it was less than two months since he had been there before.

Jim did not realise that at first. When the old lady opened her door, he swept off his greasy cap and grinned.

'Hello, there, my dear. Dodds is the name. Jim Dodds. I'm looking round for any odd nick-nacks you may have.

Bits of furniture, old pots—stuff like that.'

'I know.' She nodded.

'You know me?' Jim's grin faded. 'Someone been talking?'

'You've been here before. Six or seven weeks ago. Come in.'

Jim hesitated. He had forgotten all about it. Now it came back to him.

'Er—ah, yes. Now I remember.' He walked in doubtfully. 'But it wasn't you I saw.'

'No.' The old lady led him into a small, dark room. It was all coming back to him. 'It was my sister you saw then. She sold you a carving. A little figure,' the old lady went on.

'Of course.' Jim nodded. It was becoming clearer every minute. He had bought a carving. It was the little statue of a goat, done in some shiny black wood. Its eyes were tiny red stones and it had a sort of crown between its horns. Most of the things that he got from the old people he sold. But he had kept the statue. 'I did get a little figure off her. Gave her a good price.' He was getting his confidence back: 'I came back to see if she had anything else I could help her out with. Where is she?'

'Ill. In bed.' The old lady's eyes were very black and unwinking.

'Sorry to hear that. Is it a cold?'

'No. Please sit down.' She indicated a chair and he made himself comfortable. 'I wish she hadn't sold you the goat. It wasn't really hers, you see. It belonged to our master. She's been worried over it ever since. That's what has made her ill. You don't still have it, do you? I'd be willing to buy it back. I'd pay more than you gave for it.'

'What?' Something had just caught Jim's eye. 'Have I still got it? No. Gave it away. To a friend. Couldn't get it back now. He's gone off somewhere.' He had only heard her question and had not paid much attention to the rest of her remarks. There was a most interesting picture hanging on the wall. He wondered how he had missed noticing it last time. He could hardly keep his hands off it.

'That's a pity. She would like it back. She misses it a great deal. It was very close to her heart, you see.'

'Yes, yes. I'm sorry.' He was still only half hearing her. 'That picture up there—how long have you had it?'

'A long time. Why?'

'Do you want a bit of money for it? Not doing you much good hanging there, is it?' He laughed in what he hoped was a friendly way.

'Do you really want to buy it?' She was smiling at him. A thin smile.

'Give you thirty—forty pence for it.'

It was surprisingly easy. She seemed to forget about her sister at once. She took down the picture and dusted it for him. He got it for forty pence. He did not look for anything else. He took the painting straight out to his battered old car and drove off. He was half afraid that she would change her mind. But, as he left, she was standing at the door of her cottage, her thin hands twisted in her apron and that same thin smile on her lips.

He knew before he got home that this was another thing that he would not want to sell. He spent some minutes looking at it when he got home. He looked at it a good many more times that evening. And, when he went to bed, he felt he could not bear to be parted from it. He hung it in his bedroom.

It was a painting of a moonlight scene. There were spidery trees surrounding a white building. This looked like a temple. It had pillars holding up its roof and some of the pillars had fallen and broken. Beyond the temple there were mountains and the night sky hung over all. There were three figures in the painting. The moonlight made them stand out against the darker background. They wore long, greyish-looking cloaks which covered up their heads. He could not see their faces and he could not tell whether they were men or women. He had an odd feeling that two of them were women.

He could not take his eyes off the picture. It was the last thing he saw before he turned off the light and went to sleep.

He dreamed. At least, he thought he was dreaming. He was in bed, lying as he had done when he had fallen asleep. But he could see his bedroom clearly. It was filled by a weird, flickering light.

He sat up with a gasp. The picture had grown. It filled the whole of the opposite wall. And it was no longer a picture. It was reality. He could see the branches of the trees fluttering in the slight breeze and the clouds moving in the moonlight. The robes or cloaks that the figures were wearing were stirring, too. The figures themselves were moving.

They stepped out of the picture and came towards his bed. He could not move. All strength left him and he sank back on his pillow. They stood over him. Their hoods still hid their faces but he could see the glint of their eyes in the shadow. And he could see their hands. Long, pale and bony, they reached out for him. They seemed more like claws than hands. Their nails tore open his pyjama jacket and he screamed as they dug into his skin.

His scream held both terror and pain. The fingers sank deep into his flesh. He felt his ribs split and crack.

When the hands rose again, he saw that they held his still-beating heart. They gripped and squeezed. In his agony he could not speak or breathe.

'Where is it?' a thin, cracked voice asked.

'The goat!' another demanded.

From somewhere he found the words and the breath to speak them.

'Downstairs,' he moaned. 'Black tin box. In the table drawer.'

Two of the figures glided away. The third still held his heart for him to see, gripped in those iron talons. The pain wrenched and twisted him. It seemed centuries before they returned.

One of them held up the tiny statue of the goat. All three threw back their heads and laughed in triumph. Their hoods fell back. Two faces he knew. They were the faces of the old lady and her sister from whom he had bought the statue and the picture. The third head, horned and hairy, was not human at all.

In that nightmare moment, the thin bony fingers gave one last savage clutch at his heart and released him. Pain burned him like a lightning flash and he knew nothing more.

The woman who cleaned the house for Jim found him next morning. The doctor she called said he was lucky to have survived a heart attack like that. When Jim was well enough again to talk, he asked them to take the picture out of his room. There were no figures in it, then. He knew that there wouldn't be. There was no little statue of a goat in his tin box, either, when he got up enough courage to look.

Jim is a changed man now. He has given up buying and selling. He works in an old people's home. He has his own room there. It is kept very bare, with no pictures on the walls.

He is good with the old people and most of them like him. Some of the old ladies, however, are a bit uneasy with him. They say that he is so extremely polite that he seems almost scared of them.

Think It Over

How did Jim Dodds make his living? What would some people have called him?

Why did he not go back to places he had visited?

How would the old women from whom he bought things feel about him?

What was the name of the village he visited twice?

What had Jim bought on his first visit to the cottage?
Why should the old lady not have sold the thing?
What did Jim want to buy on this second visit?
Why did the second old lady smile as he left?
How did Jim feel about the thing he had bought this second
    time?
Where did he put it when he got it home?
What had happened to it, when Jim woke during the night?
Who came out of it? What did they want? What did they
    look like?
What had happened in the picture the next morning?
Would Jim go back to the cottage a third time? Why?
Where does Jim work now?
How does he feel about the people he works among?

Do You Know?

Who thought Jim was a clever man? What does that tell you
    about him?
What is pewter made from? Can you find out? What does it
    look like?
What sort of insects eat furniture? How can you get rid of
    them?
What is the name of a London firm that auctions old fur-
    niture and pictures? How does an auction sale work?
Where is your nearest antique shop? What sort of things are
    sold there?
Why do you think Jim went back to the village of Markell?
    Who were the two old ladies in the cottage?
Was the carving really a goat? Could it have represented
    something else? What?
What might the red stones in the carving be made of?
Why had the first old lady fallen ill? Who was the 'master'?
Do you think the picture had been in the cottage on Jim's
    first visit? Why?

Why did Jim lie to the second old lady? Did she believe him? How do you know?

Why was she willing to sell the picture? Why did Jim like the picture so much?

What might have been the predominant colour of the picture? Who was the third figure with the two old ladies?

Name two famous painters.

Why is Jim frightened of old people?

Using Words

'its eyes.' When does *its* have an apostrophe?

Put each of these words in a separate sentence: interesting, noticing, figure, centuries.

'The night sky hung over all.' How else could you phrase that?

The name for things like old silver, old pictures and old furniture is ant . . . The place where things from old times are kept is a mus . . .

What is the name 'Jim' short for? How many other names can you think of that have shortened forms?

'Now it came back to him.' What is another way of saying this?

Punctuate:

i know she nodded you know me jims grin faded someone been talking youve been here before six or seven weeks ago come in jim hesitated he had forgotten all about it now it came back to him er ah yes now i remember he walked in doubtfully but it wasnt you i saw

What sort of animals have talons and what sort have claws?

Write Now

Write a story about something old you have at home.

In play-form write the conversation the two old ladies might have had after the first one had sold the carving.

Make a list of valuable metals.

Write a poem called 'Moonlight' or 'The Face in the Picture'.

Write a story about finding a valuable antique.

Describe or draw a witch's hand.

Gravestones

. . . A man, grey-faced and looking sick, stood there . . .

It was still very early in the morning. He was standing by the window when he woke up. He could see the yard. The light was pale and cold.

'What are you doing?' his wife asked sleepily from the bed.

'I was dreaming. I dreamed that I was working down there in the yard. When I woke up I was here by the window.'

'Come back to bed.' She looked at the clock. 'It's not six yet. Get some more sleep.'

'I was carving a tombstone. There was a man with me. God! I was scared. I still am.'

'Dreams don't mean anything.' She yawned and turned on her side. 'Lie down again. Try to sleep.' Her voice died away.

He got back into bed. But he did not sleep. At about a quarter to seven he got up and went downstairs. Quietly, he made some tea. He sat at the kitchen table and drank it. There were few noises—a car passed, the clock ticked. He seemed alone in a dead world. And yet—everything was as usual. Outside the kitchen window he could see his business sign. 'Robert Boland and Son', it said, 'Stonemasons'. Everything was normal. He still felt frightened.

He was the son, Jack Boland. His father, Robert Boland, was dead. But the business went on. Like his father he was a stonemason. He carved stones for buildings, stones for ornament. Sometimes he made headstones for graves.

He had been doing that in the dream. Unlike most dreams, it did not fade. It was still clear and sharp and eerie in his mind. He rubbed his face and sighed.

It had been neither night nor day in the yard. A cold light had filled the place. He was working on a gravestone. He knew that he had to carve some words. But he did not know what they were. The man was standing behind him and he turned to ask. He had not looked at the man before. Now he saw that he wore clothes of whitish grey. The face was white, too, dead-looking. He could not see the eyes. They were deep in shadow. Then he had woken up by the window in the bedroom.

He pushed his cup away and stood up. In his pyjamas and dressing gown he went out into the yard. It was frosty and the frost gleamed on the stones. But he did not notice the cold. He searched the yard. Nothing had changed. In the dream the gravestone had been by the shed. There was nothing there now. He went back inside. It was after seven. Still troubled, he began to get ready for the day.

As the hours went by, it slowly passed from his mind. He did not talk about it to his wife. He would never have mentioned such a thing to Frank. Frank was a lad who worked for him. He saw no one else all day. He had work to do. It was a block of stone for a building. That, too, helped to take his mind off tombstones. By the end of the week he had forgotten the dream completely.

Then, one night, he had the dream again. Again he was working on the same tombstone. The same pale customer stood over him. This time in the dream he knew the words. But when he woke he could not remember what they had been.

Again it was very vivid. He woke this time in bed. But he got up to switch on the light. He had been sure, lying awake there in the dark, that his hands were covered in stone dust. Yet, when he saw them under the light, they were quite clean. His wife did not wake. Afterwards he could not sleep. But, even when the first light came, he did not get up. He was afraid to look out into the yard.

He hardly spoke to his wife at breakfast. He heard Frank

arrive, whistling, in the yard. But he put off going out as long as he could. But at last he had to go out to work.

Out in the yard he almost laughed with relief. There was no tombstone leaning against the shed. He had been so sure that he would see one there. He went eagerly to work.

The relief made it so much worse when he went into the shed. He could not speak for a moment. It felt as though someone had punched him over the heart. Then he found his voice.

'Frank!' he shouted and then, more angrily, 'Frank!'

'What's up, boss?' Frank had run into the shed and stood staring at him.

'Did you put this here?' He heard his own voice tremble.

'What?'

'This! This thing—this gravestone?'

'That, boss? Yes. But that's not a gravestone.'

Boland turned. It was dark in the shed. His eyes had played him tricks. It was just a short wide plank of wood.

'I brought it in here last night,' Frank explained. 'It was getting wet out in the yard. Why? What's up?'

'Nothing,' he said. 'Nothing. It's all right. You can get back to work.'

Frank left him. It was a minute or two before he could carry on. His heart was thumping in his chest. But he went back to work, too. By the time evening came he had almost forgotten his scare of the morning. The days went by. The dream became a faint uneasiness right at the back of his mind.

The third time, the dream did not end. He woke from it to find himself in the yard. He could tell from the light in the sky that it was nearly dawn. He was in his overalls and his hands were white with dust. He was quite alone.

But the headstone was there. There was light enough to see it clearly. He could even make out the words he had carved on it. But he did not need to read them. He knew what they would be. He would see his own name and a date.

'John Boland—Born 1st August 1922. Died—' The date of his death was not on the stone.

So—he was safe. He had wakened from the dream in time. And he knew what he had to do. But there must be no mistake. He could break the stone up with a heavy hammer. But that wasn't it. It had to be destroyed completely. Fortunately he also knew just how to do that.

He got the truck out. The stone was heavy. But he could save himself, now. That thought gave him strength. He slid the headstone into the back of the truck. He opened the gates of the yard and drove out. He thought he heard his wife call to him. But he did not stop. There was no time to waste.

He would throw the stone over Mitton Quarry. He would pick a rock face where there had been blasting. Then it would go with all the other broken stone into the grinders. It would be powdered up. That would be the end of it and of all his dreaming. There would no longer be a feeling of danger hanging over him.

There was little colour yet in the landscape. It was still not light enough for that. He saw no one. The land was empty, soundless. There was no wind. All the trees stood motionless against the sky. It was a pale, cold morning.

The watchman at Mitton Quarry had been having a cup of tea. In an hour or two he would go off duty. The sudden knocking at the door of his hut made him jump. He opened it. A man, grey-faced and looking sick, stood there.

'What is it?' he asked.

'Up there!' the man gasped, pointing to the rim of the quarry. 'I'm on my way to Bristol—at least, I was. I'd set off early in the car. On the top road there I saw a man. Walking along. There was something stiff about him. He looked—blind—like a sleepwalker. I stopped the car and shouted. He was so near the edge of the quarry.' The motorist stopped and gulped. 'He didn't hear. Didn't stop. Walked right over the edge.'

'Come on,' cried the watchman. 'Show me where.'

The early morning light was brightening quickly. It was not hard to find the body. It lay flat on its back among stones. One stone stood upright at its head. The watchman bent over the sprawled shape. The motorist stood back. When he cried out the watchman looked at him.

'What's wrong?' he said.

'That stone.' The motorist pointed. 'Like a gravestone.'

'Yes,' the watchman said. 'Same shape. What of it? It's just—chance.'

'I know,' the motorist told him. 'It must have shaken me badly. Just for a moment—I was seeing things. I swear I saw something on the stone. Writing. Carved on. There was a name—Roland or Boland or something. And a date. Clear as clear. 1st August 1922 and "Died: 7th March 1976."'

'That's today,' said the watchman. He looked at the stone. For a long moment they were both silent. 'There's nothing there that I can see,' he said.

'No.' The motorist shook his head. 'It was—just for a second. It's gone now.'

The watchman had examined the body and now he stood up. He shook his head. 'We'd best get back to the hut,' he said. 'You need a cup of tea. Must have been a terrible shock, seeing a thing like this.' He looked at the height of the quarry towering above them.

'I wonder why he did it,' said the motorist. 'Suicide? Or just an accident? Hadn't we better get the police and an ambulance?'

'Won't make much difference now,' said the watchman sadly. 'He must have been killed instantly.' He looked down at the body. Dust lay thick on the face and clothes of the dead man. 'Poor chap,' he said. 'He's a goner. He's dead. Stone dead.'

Think It Over

What had wakened the man up?

What did his wife think about dreams?

Why did he not sleep when he went back to bed?

What was his job?

Why was the dream he had unlike other dreams?

What did he have to carve on the gravestone in his dream?

What sort of clothes was the man in his dream wearing?

What sort of a morning was it when he went out into the yard?

Why did he examine his hands when he woke up from the second dream?

Why was he afraid to look in the yard?

What was the name of the lad who worked for him?

How had he made the mistake about the piece of wood?

What was strange about the third dream?

What words had he carved on the gravestone? What was missing?

How did he lift the heavy stone on his own? Where was he going to get rid of it?

Where was the motorist going?

What did Boland look like when the motorist saw him on the rim of the quarry?

Do You Know?

Where does the sun rise in the morning?

Why are tombstones put at the head of graves?

What is the difference between a mason and a bricklayer? What other workmen get very dusty?

How is stone cut into blocks? How do you carve stone? How does frost split stone?

Are there any ornamental carvings in stone on any buildings you know?

How long do you remember your dreams? Can you remember a dream you had last night?

Who might the man in Boland's dream have been? Do you
    see any significance in the colour of his clothes?
How do you know that the motorist is out of breath?
Have your eyes ever played you tricks? What happened?
How are heavy pieces of stone usually moved about?
What would the grinders in the quarry be used for? What
    might the stone from the quarry be for?
What sort of day takes all the colour out of a landscape?

Using Words

'Sign.' How many different meanings can you find for this
    word? Use them in sentences.
'It's not six yet.' 'At about a quarter to seven.' How many
    other ways can you think of to tell someone roughly what
    time it is?
Use here and hear correctly in sentences of your own.
A boy who is working to learn a trade is an app . . .
What other words do you know meaning dead including
    slang words?
'It had been neither night nor day in the yard.' Use neither,
    nor and either, or in sentences of your own.
'What's up, boss?' What other words mean boss?
Use each of these, correctly spelt, in sentences of your own:
    completely, fortunately, thought, broken, ambulance.
Give another word for truck.
'. . . he got up to switch on the light.' How many other
    expressions can you think of which use the word switch?
    Use each in a sentence.
'It felt as though someone had punched him over the
    heart.' Complete the following:
    After the football match, he felt as though he . . .
    Sitting in the dentist's chair, he felt as though . . .
    When he came off his bike, it felt as though . . .

Write Now

In play-form, write the conversation a policeman might
   have with Mrs Boland, when he tells her about the death.

Describe the view from your bedroom window at half-light. It
   could be early morning or evening. What different colours
   might you see in the sky?

Make a list of tradesmen who would make things in a village
   in the last century.

Describe the scene in your classroom at the present moment
   OR describe all the noises you can hear inside and outside the school.

Write a poem called 'Gravestones' or 'Work'.

The writing on a headstone is called an epitaph. Do you
   know any interesting epitaphs?

The Mouth

. . . He could see the breath and the great lolling tongue . . .

The poacher was pleased when he shot the rabbit. He gave a little grunt of joy. It was so big. It would make a fine Sunday dinner.

He had been after it for some time. He was not sure which holes formed its burrow. He would see it just for fleeting moments. Then it had scurried away. Vanished sometimes into thin air. Indeed it seemed to have the speed of a hare. It could also twist and turn like the hare.

He prided himself on knowing the ways of rabbits. That was the art of being a poacher; to think like your prey; to know which way an animal would run. But this big buck rabbit had had the better of him for the past year. It always turned in the opposite direction to which his gun was pointing; it went to earth as swiftly as a fox. It had once run in water, too, like a fox putting the dogs off his scent. This was odd, because rabbits hate water.

But now he had shot it. It was an evening when the sun was on fire in the western evening sky. The rabbit was suddenly silhouetted in the dipping sun. He had fired immediately and his heart leapt when he saw it fall rather than dodge away.

He went to it. There it was; dead in the grass. He had caught it in the head. The shot had gone straight through one eye socket.

But there was an odd thing about it; its mouth was open as though it was caught in the middle of a yawn. This was unusual; a dead rabbit's mouth is usually shut. He could see all the teeth and right down the throat. The tongue was lolling out to one side.

Yes, it certainly was big. The biggest rabbit he had ever

seen. Maybe it was the king of the rabbits. He grinned to himself and patted his stomach.

The sun had gone down, leaving burning embers in the western sky. He had three miles to go back through the forest. But there should be no danger from the landowner at this time of day. His forester, too, should be having his tea.

He had gone about a hundred metres into the depth of some pine trees when he had the impression he was being followed. As a poacher he had an instinct for such things. But he was a tough character and he was sure, too, that he could outwit any forester or gamekeeper. He glanced back over his shoulder and quickened his pace.

As he did so, he had the fleeting impression of a shape in a tree behind him. It was in a tree on the forest's edge, flecked with the rays of the dying sun. It was a shape about a metre across with white round the edges. It was only a quick impression and then it was gone. He slowed again. There was no sight of a human following.

But the feeling of being followed persisted. He had gone about a mile, now, deep into the forest. Mosquitoes were bothering him and he was surprised that he did not know the path as well as he thought. He had stumbled several times on branches and roots of trees and tripped in several holes.

He looked round again. The same big shape was visible between the branches of an oak tree. It is easy to see a face in an oak tree, but this was different. It was slightly clearer now and the white was strongest at the top and there was something pink in the middle. He still put it down, though, to his imagination and the failing light. But he quickened his pace once more.

He fell almost immediately, catching his foot in a root. His ankle was badly wrenched but he got up. He could still walk on it but it was very painful. As he stumbled on, he first heard the sound. It was a soft, gentle sound of breathing. He told himself it was the wind blowing through the upper

44

branches of the forest. But it had the in-out rhythm of breathing rather than the constant sigh of the wind. He started to run despite the pain in his ankle.

Bats dipped and flicked across his face. He had bad stitch and he had to pause for a moment to catch his breath. This time he could hear the sound of breathing even above his own panting. He glanced round once more. It was fully dark now and the moon was visible between the branches. But despite the darkness he could see the shape once more, some fifty metres away. This time it was very clear. It had the definite shape of a mouth. No body of anything could be seen. But he could see pink bared gums and the teeth seemed to flash. Breath could be seen coming from the mouth.

One part of his brain told him it was all in his imagination. Perhaps he had been poaching too much lately and not had enough sleep. But the other part sent fear deep into his gut. It was the ancient fear of the hunted.

He ran as fast as he could down the forest ride. Brambles seemed to leap out and scratch his face. Bats still zig-zagged across in front of him. But it was the sound of the breathing that really frightened him.

He glanced round once more. The mouth was no more than thirty metres behind him now. He could see it clearly in the wide ride. It could be no tree shape now. It bobbed up and down. It had two big teeth at the top. They looked like a guillotine waiting to fall. Thank God he was only a short distance from the forest edge.

He leapt the gate at the end of the ride and ran into the blessed open space of the field. He felt the thing must disappear when he had left the forest. But, no. There was the giant mouth, bobbing over the gate. He fell to his knees and fired his gun into it.

But in his gut he knew a gun was no use. The mouth came on. He could see the breath and the great lolling tongue.

He turned in a last desperate attempt to run to the safety

of his cottage whose lights he could now see. But now his ankle gave way, he could feel a hot wind on his neck and something licked across an ear. He rolled over on to his back. He had the impression of looking down a tunnel. The tunnel's edge was flanged with sharp teeth. A large pink tongue shot out and gripped him round the waist. Then . . .

His wife found the body the next morning. The head was several metres away. It had been cut off cleanly. No other damage was done to the body. All round the body the grass was closely cropped.

The wife was held in custody for a short while and then released. They said she could not have had the strength to cut off a head like that. The coroner's court could not understand why the cut was so clean. It was put down as murder by a person or persons unknown.

Think It Over

What pleased the poacher about shooting the rabbit?
What was unusual about the rabbit?
What did the poacher pride himself on?
At what time of day did he shoot it?
What was odd about the dead rabbit?
How far was the poacher away from his home?
How far had he gone before he felt he was being followed?
What did he have a fleeting impression of?
What surprised him when he had gone about a mile?
How did he sprain his ankle?
At first what did he think the strange sound was?
What did the shape look like after he had started to run?
What frightened him more than the bats?
What did the teeth in the mouth look like?
Why did he feel better when he ran into the field?
How did the thing catch him?
How did he die?

What happened to the poacher's wife?
What did the coroner think had happened?

Do You Know?

What does a poacher do?
List some of the differences between a rabbit and a hare.
Name some other animals besides rabbits that hate water.
What kind of gun might the poacher have been using?
What sort of job does a forester do?
What work does a gamekeeper do?
What kind of country do mosquitoes breed in?
Have you ever wrenched your ankle? What happened?
At what time of day do bats fly? What are they doing while
    they are flying around? Where do they sleep?
What causes a stitch in the side? How do you get rid of it?
How do you know the air had gone cold when he saw the
    mouth about fifty metres away?
What is a forest ride?
Name one place near you where brambles grow. Have you
    ever picked the berries? At what time of the year are they
    ready?
Why might the grass have been closely cropped all round
    the body?
What animals' teeth do you find the most frightening?

Using Words

One rabbit lives in a burrow.Many rabbits live together in
    their war . . .
grunt. What other sounds that are wordless can you make
    with your mouth?
Write and spell the days of the week correctly.
Something that lasts for a short time lasts for a fl . . . mo-

ment. You will find the missing word in the story.

A fox lives in an earth. A badger lives in a s . . . A hare lives in a f . . .

What is a silhouette?

'. . . the sun was on fire in the western evening sky.' Write a similar descriptive phrase about a sunrise.

Complete these sentences of your own:

He ran as fast as . . .

The sunset was like . . .

The tunnel was as black as . . .

The head was cut off as clean as . . .

'throat.' Make a list of *oa* words.

'He still put it down to his imagination . . .' What other meaning does the phrase 'put it down' have? Use 'put it out' and 'put it over' in two separate sentences.

A repeated pattern of sound is a 'hhtrmy'. Sort out these letters into the word in the story.

What is a guillotine? Is it still used? Has it a second meaning?

Use each of these words in a sentence of your own: character, impression, immediately, disappear.

Write Now

A large pink tongue came out and gripped him round the waist. Then . . . Describe what happened after that in sentences of your own.

Find out what you can about bats and write a short article about them.

Write a poem called 'The Bats in the Tower'.

You are alone in the woods at night with a sprained ankle. Describe how you feel and how you get home.

What happened to the mouth afterwards? Did anyone else see it? Did it attack again? Did it disappear? Write down your own version of what happened.

If you have ever been hunting, write down some advice for a person who wants to take up the sport.

The Devil's Mound

. . . they came to a great roaring wind and a terror that made them run for their lives . . .

I remember that afternoon. I wish I could turn time back. I was free, then. Nothing threatened me.

I had been walking all day. Coming off the moors, I had twisted my ankle. It was giving me a lot of pain. It was late afternoon and the shadows were growing long. The air was heavy and there was thunder about. I was limping along a narrow road, hoping that it would bring me to a village. It brought me to Wychwood Manor and to Bowman and to terror.

When I saw the house, I knew that I had gone wrong. I was not on a country road. It was the driveway to the Manor. It ran through trees and then led across an open space of lawns and paths up to the door.

I knocked. No one came. The pain in my ankle had grown worse. The air seemed heavier. I had an odd feeling that something was watching me from among the trees. But I could see nothing. I knocked again.

At last there was a rattle of bolts and the door opened part way. It was held by a chain on the inside.

'What do you want?' The old, white-haired man who showed his face round the door looked scared.

I explained what had happened. Could I use their 'phone? Could I ring for a taxi, perhaps? I would, of course, pay.

'No.' His voice trembled. He was about to close the door.

'Wait, please!' I begged. 'How far is the nearest village?'

'Five miles.'

I could not have walked another five yards.

'Five miles! I've got to have help. I can hardly walk: I'll

just have to sit on this step till morning, if you won't let me in.'

'You won't do that,' he said.

'Who is it, Homerton? Don't let it in!' That was another voice. I called. Desperately I explained again what had happened. Another face, a younger one, looked out at me. Then the door closed. I knocked and shouted.

It seemed a long time before it opened again on its chain. A hand came out.

'Take it!' one of them ordered. I did and stood there in surprise, looking at the crucifix in my hand. Then I was given a book. 'Read!' the voice said. 'Read it aloud.'

I read the passage. It was about being delivered from evil spirits. At last the chain rattled and the door opened. I went in.

Things were a bit more normal for a time after that. Homerton, the old servant, helped me to a chair in the library. All the curtains were drawn and lights were burning in there. I was given food. Homerton even put a rough bandage on my ankle. Bowman, the owner of the house, sat with me while I ate and drank. He said little but he did tell me that there was no 'phone in the house. He did not say how I could get down to the village.

My uneasiness returned. It was strange to be sitting in a curtained room when it was daylight outside. Bowman and his servant, Homerton, were very odd, too. But my fears went deeper than that.

Homerton came to take away my empty tray. Bowman went with him to the door. They went outside. I heard them muttering together. With the bandage my ankle felt stronger. Something made me limp to the window and draw back the curtain.

'Don't open the window!' Bowman's voice was shrill. But I did not drop the curtain and turn round. I could not have done so.

I was watching something on the drive. It seemed to be a cloud of tiny black dots. They spread out thinly and then flowed together. The thing moved towards the house and then suddenly vanished among the trees.

Bowman pushed me aside and looked out. 'Did you see it? What did it look like?' His hand was gripping my shoulder hard.

I freed myself and moved away. 'I don't know,' I said. 'Was it a swarm of bees?'

'Bees!' he gave a short laugh which was without humour.

'What was it, then?' I asked.

It had been a few days since he had talked to anyone but Homerton. He began slowly but once he had begun he did not stop.

In the grounds of the manor there was a small hill. Men had made it many centuries ago. Local people called it the Devil's Mound and there were many legends about it. Some said that it was a burial mound. Others spoke of an old temple. Strange gods—or demons—had been worshipped there. Men had tried to open the mound and come to a bad end. Bowman's great-grandfather had been one. And he, too, had died.

'I thought I knew better than the men who had gone before me,' Bowman went on. 'I read old papers and books about the legends. My great-grandfather had left a diary. It told of the dark force in Devil's Mound. I read deeply in such matters. I thought that, with all my knowledge, I would be safe. I thought that I would be able to control that evil force, to use it. I should have left well alone.'

Bowman and his servant, Homerton, had opened the mound. They had used words and rituals Bowman had found in old books of black magic. They had thought themselves safe. They had been wrong.

When they broke into the mound they came to a roaring wind and a terror that made them run for their lives. They reached the manor house safely. But they had lived in fear ever since.

'It seems to me that it is a thing which lives in a twilight world between this one and the next,' Bowman went on. 'It does not see all men clearly. You came and did not feel its presence.'

I said nothing.

'But some faces it sees,' he said. 'It hears some voices. Then it will not rest until it has destroyed them.'

I believed him completely. I asked the obvious question, 'Why did it let you live?'

'Its power is weak in daylight. But it grows strong after dark. Then it makes itself known.'

'How?' I whispered.

'By a gale, a howling. You will find out.'

'But it can't get in?' I asked.

'Not so far.' His face was set and pale. 'To my understanding it cannot get into a house protected by magic or the marks of religion, unless it is invited.' He stopped and nodded. 'Unless it is invited in. That's why we kept you waiting at the door until we were sure that you were what you seemed to be.'

'When did it happen?' I asked. 'When did you free it?'

'Three days ago.'

'And you have been prisoners ever since?'

'Yes. Homerton tried to get down to the village a day ago. He didn't get far. That's why we let you in at last. When we were sure that you were not—that thing. If your ankle is strong enough tomorrow, perhaps you would help us?'

'Yes.' I did not feel eager. 'What is it you want? A priest? Perhaps he can lay the thing to rest again.'

'Not a priest.' Bowman shook his head. 'Maybe some food, some supplies. A priest could do no good. Before he died, my great-grandfather had filled up the hole in the mound. He lay outside. He had died by his own hand. Somehow he had discovered something about that—that demon out there.' Bowman pointed to the window. His finger shook slightly. 'He had written in his diary. It wants human lives. If they are not given willingly, it will take them.

54

But that is the only way it can be imprisoned again. The man who sets it free must sacrifice himself.'

We did not talk much after that. When full night came, Homerton brought me blankets. Because of my ankle, I slept downstairs. I was left alone.

I did not sleep well. A wind—if it was a wind—got up outside. In my half sleep it sounded more like the crying out of madmen or the howling of animals as it beat on and rattled the window panes. But it was a human voice which woke me completely at last. And it was calling my name.

I got up, put on the light and went over to the window. The shouts were just outside. When I pulled back the curtain, I saw Homerton. His face was chalk white against the darkness behind him and he was crying out in mortal terror.

'For God's sake, let me in! Open the door! Help me!'

I, too, felt his terror. I hobbled to the front door. The key was in the lock. I turned it and wrestled back the bolts. Homerton stood on the steps.

'What are you doing out there?' I gabbled. I had no time to say more. It was not Homerton. It grew and changed. I glimpsed the open mouth. It seemed full of coarse hair. The eyes were pits of green fire. Then there was only a great rushing wind.

It picked me up and threw me against the wall. I felt my head crack. Then there was blackness and nothing.

It could not have lasted long. I came back to myself to hear a scream. Bowman was half-running, half-falling down the stairs. The wind seemed loud enough to burst my ears. The air around him was full of flying objects, a small table, a twisting rug, the heavy curtains, torn from their hangings. As he reached the foot of the stairs, these curtains hovered over him like birds of prey. Then they enwrapped him. There was one last awful scream.

Something crashed into me again. My head seemed to burst. I knew no more until I woke to see the grey light of morning.

I managed to struggle part of the way to the village. A farmer found me. When a party of men went back to the manor, they found Homerton's dead body as well as his master's. Homerton had been battered and mangled, too.

For a while I was sure that they suspected me of the murder of the two men. I could see, though, that some of them half-believed me. The legends of the Devil's Mound were well-known in the village.

They believed me, however, when a doctor had examined both bodies. He said that I would have to have been both a giant and a madman to cause injuries like that.

In fact, I heard what he muttered to the police sergeant. No human strength could have crushed and broken the bones of both men in that way.

So the police let me go home. They will want me back for the inquest. I don't know if I shall be able to attend. I have been followed.

Bowman did not die as a willing sacrifice. The thing has not been laid to rest. He said that it lived in a twilight world but that it could see some faces. It has seen mine and it has heard my voice. Why it did not kill me, too, on that dreadful night I do not know. Perhaps it was too eager for its other victims. But it is aware of me. It is eager for me now.

I know that it can change its shape. One day I shall open my door to a neighbour, to a friend, to some public official. Unthinking, I shall invite them in. But I shall not be asking anything human in. I shall be inviting death.

My only hope is to cut myself off entirely from the world and other people. Can I do that? Can anyone?

I live alone on a tree-lined road. It is evening now. The breeze outside is growing stronger. It is making the branches move about. It is beginning to have a strange whistle to it.

Down the road in the shadows under the trees there, there is a darker shadow. It is shaped neither like a man nor like an animal. But it is not just a shadow. And it is waiting.

Think It Over

What had the writer been doing all day? Why was he in pain?

What was he hoping to find as he walked along the narrow road?

Where did the road actually lead?

What happened when he knocked on the door at first.

Who was in the house?

How far away was the nearest village? Could the writer have walked there?

What did he have to do before he was allowed into the house?

What was strange about the library?

What happened when he drew back the curtain?

At first what did he think he saw in the driveway?

Why had Bowman opened the mound?

Whose diary had Bowman read? What other books had he and Homerton read before they opened the mound?

When they broke into the mound, what happened?

How long have they been prisoners?

How can the thing be imprisoned again?

What was it that awakened the writer at last?

Who did he think he was letting into the house? Who did he really let in? What happened to him then?

How did Bowman die?

Who found the writer in the morning? What did people suspect at first?

Had the thing been laid to rest? Where is it at the end of the story?

Do You Know?

What are moors? Why might it be dangerous to go walking on lonely moors by oneself? What should you do before setting off on a walk like that?

What is the treatment for a twisted ankle?

Why did the air seem heavy that afternoon? What does a heaviness in the air usually foretell?

What sort of things make a person's voice tremble?

What was Homerton's position in the house?

Why did he tell the writer that he would not sit on the step till morning?

What might the book have been that the writer was given to read from?

How do you know that the people in the house have no means of transport?

When do bees swarm? What makes them swarm?

Name a famous man-made mound in Britain. What are usually found in prehistoric mounds?

Bowman says that the writer did not feel the presence of the thing from the mound at first. Was he right? Why?

What force does a gale measure on the Beaufort Scale?

Why did the evil spirit not kill the writer at once?

Using Words

'The driveway to the Manor.' How many words can you think of to describe a course that people can travel on?

'terror.' List six words ending -or.

The study of ancient remains is called arch . . .

Use each of these words in a separate sentence: surprise, uneasiness, humour, laid, knowledge.

What is the difference between hobbling and limping?

'Then there was blackness and nothing.' Write this another way.

Name some birds of prey.

How many 'public officials' who call at people's houses can you list?

Write Now

Write about how you feel when you sense a coming
thunderstorm and what it is like to be in the storm when
it breaks.

Describe or draw the thing that came out of the mound.

Draw a plan of the manor, the drive and the mound.

Write a story about something terrifying on the moors.

Would you like to turn time back? What would you do, if
you could? Write an account.

You have a puncture while cycling in the country. You call at
this old house and . . .

Dunk and Spadger

. . . it seemed like a scream from a nightmare . . .

The building from the outside looked like a school: one storey, with plenty of big glass windows; a typical primary school. The fence was different though: eight feet high with barbed-wire on the top.

'It's going to be tricky,' said Spadger.

'Let's leave it,' said Dunk.

'No,' said Titch. 'We don't want to let it beat us.'

Spadger and Titch were thirteen-year-olds; Dunk was twelve. They had taken to breaking into schools at night. They had done most of the schools in their own area and on this night had moved across to the other side of the town.

'It said in the paper they were going to improve security,' remarked Dunk.

'That was dogs,' said Titch. 'No dogs here; they would have heard us by now.'

'Let's try the back,' said Spadger.

They crept round to the back.

Titch did it for the smoking. He had been caned for smoking. He liked to sit in the teacher's chair and smoke cigarette after cigarette, lighting each from the butt of the last. It gave him a big kick, he said.

Spadger liked the getting in and out part. He read every prisoner-of-war book he could lay his hands on. What he liked, once inside, was trying to open locked doors and cupboards. He never took anything; it was just the challenge of seeing if he could open things.

Dunk liked libraries. He collected pictures of animals. He tore them out of library books and stuck them in a big book at home. He did not like breaking in at all. His Mum would not let him keep pets. This was the nearest he could get to it.

'It's just as difficult here,' said Spadger. The high fence was in front of them. 'But I'm going over.' He had various tools including a homemade pair of wire cutters. 'I can cut the wire at the top. It's too thick down the bottom here.'

Dunk gave him a bunk-up. He could just get a toe-hold with his plimsolls in the wire diamonds. With a quick scramble, he was up at the top hacking away at the barbed-wire. Dunk and Titch kept watch.

A light flashed some fifty metres away. 'Scarper,' whispered Titch. Spadger scrambled down. They hid in a clump of brambles and gorse.

Someone in uniform came by, flashing a torch on the wire fence.

'A Kraut,' whispered Spadger, when he had gone. He called all cops Krauts on an evening like this. In the darkness he could not see the difference in the uniform between a policeman and a Securicor man.

They heard a van drive away. They waited a few minutes and then Spadger was back at the top hacking away. 'Sod it!' he said. He had jagged his hand on the wire; blood dripped down his jeans and on to his plimsolls. 'Gi' us a hanky,' he asked the others. Dunk passed up a dirty hanky.

Soon Dunk and Titch heard the low whistle. Two strands of the barbed-wire were cut. They knew they could follow him over. Titch helped Dunk up on to the top of the fence. As he straddled the top, Dunk was in two minds as to whether to drop back down again and run home. But his father was probably drunk. He scrambled down after Titch on the inside.

They crept up to the building. Their normal method was to break a window near a handle and let themselves in. But this building did not have handles inside the windows.

'They're getting clever,' said Spadger. But he soon found a side door. He picked away at the lock but he could not open it. 'We'll have to try the roof,' he said.

'Let's go home,' said Dunk. 'I don't like this place.'

'You would never have escaped, if you give up that easy,' said Spadger. He was soon up a drainpipe and on to the flat roof; then he was bending down to help the others up. 'Look for a skylight,' he said.

'Use the torch,' said Titch.

'No, we'll be seen for miles around,' said Spadger.

They crept into the middle of the roof. They were all standing on roughened glass, but they did not know it. It felt the same texture as the roof.

Below them in a secure room were twenty rats and three South American Wolf Spiders. The rats were in cages and the spiders in a glass case; they were being used in experiments.

The skylight should have held the weight of three men, let alone boys, but builders are often careless. In this case a builder had gone home ill and his mate did not know the right type of bolts to fit.

'Let's go,' said Dunk. 'I'm scared we'll get caught.'

'We'll find a way in,' said Spadger. 'You'll feel better inside; you always do. You'll find lots of pictures of animals.'

The Securicor man was now back in his van after visiting the carpet factory. He had some small factories to check and he had to make one more check of the Stevenson Institute for Tropical Diseases where they kept those spiders. Should he go now; or should he make it his last call for the night? He sat back in his van and lit up a cigarette.

'I could do with a fag now,' said Titch.

'You're not lighting up here,' said Spadger. 'Be seen for miles around . . . oh . . . aw . . . aw!' His voice rose to a shriek as he crashed through the skylight with the others after him. To Dunk it seemed like a scream from a nightmare, then a hard object knocking the wind out of his body, and then a smashing of glass. A cupboard had broken his and Spadger's fall, but it toppled, tipping them once more into space for a second. Titch was not so lucky.

Dunk started to cry. There was a pause while he found he was not really hurt. Then the shock overcame him and more tears flowed.

'Shut up!' said Spadger. 'We've made enough noise as it is. Strike a match, Titch. My torch has smashed.' It had crunched in his pocket and cut his thigh. But Titch did not reply. He did not reply because he was dead. His head had struck a case of spiders.

'Titch! Titch' cried Spadger.

'Is he dead?' sobbed Dunk.

'Not Titch,' said Spadger. 'Find his matches.'

They felt for him in the dark. Spadger soon got his hands in Titch's pocket and found the matches. He lit one. In the flickering light they could see Titch lying on his back. There was a big hole in his head and blood was coming out of it.

'He's dead,' said Dunk.

'Just unconscious,' said Spadger. But his voice did not have that normal cockiness. 'Titch! Titch!' The match burnt his fingers and he flung it away. He lit another. The rats' eyes glinted in the dark. 'Christ!' he yelled. 'Rats!' He dropped the match.

'Light another,' said Dunk. 'Let me see them.'

'I don't want to see!' His heart was racing and the normally cool Spadger was breathing heavily. If he lit a match he could see their evil faces; if it remained dark they could attack him and bite his throat. 'Oh, Christ!' he said pushing himself against the wall, groping for a door handle. He must get out. Out. Out.

Dunk lit a match. Spadger shielded his eyes. 'They won't hurt you,' said Dunk. 'They're in cages.'

'But we might have broken them,' gasped Spadger. He had found the handle of a door. But it would not open and he had lost his lock-picking tool in the fall. He sank to the floor, his shoulders heaving.

'They're in cages,' said Dunk. 'Don't cry, Spadger.'

But Spadger let out a shriek. Something had crossed his

leg. It was a spider from the glass case that Titch's head had smashed. It was a harmless specimen; the South American Wolf Spiders were secure, as were the rats.

'The rats are out!' shrieked Spadger.

'I'll look,' said Dunk. He struck a match. But immediately it went out. 'Damn!' he said. 'The matches are finished.'

'Oh!' whimpered Spadger.

In a nearby factory the Securicor man wondered where to go next. Should he go to the clothing depot? Or should he make his last trip round that tropical medicine place? He decided on the clothing factory.

In the secure room Dunk tried to lift the cupboard so that the could try to climb back through the roof. Spadger was of no use to him. He just sat moaning. Dunk could not manage it on his own.

'Get the rats off. Get the rats off,' moaned Spadger.

It was not rats; it was the spiders attracted by the blood on his hand and leg.

Dunk sat down by him and tried to brush them away. 'It's not rats; you're all right,' said Dunk. But Spadger did not believe him.

They sat side by side during the long night. Spadger fainted from time to time. It was six o'clock before the Securicor man found them.

'I'm not going to send you away,' said the magistrate, 'because of your long night of terror.' Dunk looked up at him. He was not really thinking about himself; he was thinking about Titch's funeral. He had seen the hearse pass down the road. 'I am going to put you on probation for two years.' His Dad would not let him go to the funeral. He would not let him go to see Spadger in hospital either.

He walked back down the road with his father. 'Now perhaps you'll behave yourself,' his father said for the hundredth time. He kicked a pile of leaves blown up by the cold wind. 'Can't I go and see Spadger, Dad?' he pleaded.

'No,' said his father, 'I'm not having you in one of those places.'

Think It Over

Why was the building not quite like a school?
Who was the youngest of the boys?
Why had the boys moved to the other side of the town?
Why did Titch like breaking into schools? Why did Spadger?
Why did Spadger cut the wire at the top?
Where might he have got his wire cutters?
What does 'wire diamonds' mean?
Who interrupted them?
Why did the van drive away?
Who was first over the wire?
Why did they not go through the side door?
What did they try next?
What was the name of the building they were at?
Why did the skylight fall in?
Who started to cry?
What had happened to Titch?
What happened to the torch? How did they get light?
Why is Spadger more afraid than Dunk?
How did Dunk try to get out again?
Why were they not punished severely?
Where is Spadger at the end of the story?

Do You Know?

How old are children who go to primary school?
Why do children break into schools? Has it ever happened at your school?
Where is your local library?
What was a 'Kraut'?
What jobs do Securicor men do?
At first who is the leader of the boys? What evidence is there?

What sort of experiments were the spiders and rats used
   for?
Who takes over the leadership when they are in the
   building?
What was the biggest danger to the boys?
Name another dangerous spider.
How do you know that the season of the year is autumn?

Using Words

Copy out one each of the abbreviations used in the story
   like: *it's*. What are each short for?
'lighting each from the butt of the last . . .' Give another
   word for *butt*.
'Prisoner-of-war.' How many other compound words do
   you know? A dictionary will help.
Why is a cupboard so called?
'With a quick scramble he was up at the top.' Write your
   own sentences using these words:
   With . . . he . . .
   With . . . she . . .
   With . . . they . . .
What slang names do you know for: a Frenchman; an
   Italian; an Englishman (in America); an Englishman (in
   Australia); a Welshman; an Irishman?
Complete this word: The Securicor man was making ran . . .
   checks.
'Gi' us a hanky.' Spell the word *hanky* in full. Check with
   your dictionary.
What is a '*strand* of wire'?
'Dunk was in two minds.' Write this another way.
What does 'texture' mean?
Punctuate this correctly: not titch said spadger find his
   matches
What is another word for moaning?

Write Now

List all the different kinds of school there are.

Write your own break-in story. Try for an unusual ending.

Write a poem called 'Rats' or 'Spiders'.

Make some signs to go outside the Institute.

Write an account of your night's work as a Securicor man.

In play-form, write the conversation Dunk might have had when the Securicor man finds them.

Write a poem called 'The Long Night' or 'Things I Hate Most'.

Inheritance

. . . a man becomes a werewolf through eating human flesh . . .

Werewolves? Who believes in such things? Nobody down in the village. Why should they? To them the story is quite clear. Sheep have been killed and at last the killer dogs have been driven away. That is how it must seem to those people in the village and in the farms around.

The Pajaks came to live in the cottage at the edge of the moor some six months ago. The could speak English. They seemed to have money to live on. Mr Pajak did not need to work. People did not see much of the family. Sometimes Mr Pajak came down to the village to shop. But he was a silent man. He returned any greeting quite politely. But he did not talk much to anyone. It was not very often that Mrs Pajak was seen in the village. The Pajaks had no friends. But they bothered no one and nobody bothered them.

Round about that time, the sheep worrying started. So, people had other things to think about than the Pajaks. It began quite a distance away at first. The raiding dogs were clever. They never struck in the same place twice and they seemed to kill for the joy of killing. A farmer would go out in the morning to find dead carcases of sheep. Some had had their throats torn out. Others would have been partly eaten. He would keep careful watch with his gun the next night. But the dogs would not visit him again.

After a time, there were many farmers keeping watch over a wide area. They would wait until dawn with loaded guns. But the dogs seemed to have a sixth sense. It was always unguarded flocks that were attacked. The police came into it, too, before long.

They found some kind of pattern to the attacks. Two or

three weeks would go by and the sheep would be left in peace. Then there would be one or two nights of savage killing. It took some time to realise that the raids happened about the night of the full moon. But no one could make anything of that.

Twice they thought they had found the culprits. An Alsatian was shot early one morning, crossing a field. But there was no sure evidence. The owner, very fond of his dog, swore that it had never attacked anything in its life. On suspicion, a Labrador belonging to two old ladies was painlessly destroyed by a vet. The old ladies insisted that it was not guilty but it made no difference.

Then the girl was found dead. She had been savaged and bitten. A full-scale enquiry followed after that. She had been returning late from a dance. She had a long, lonely road to walk through moorland. No one had heard her cries. The police checked practically every house in the area. They even came to the Pajaks' cottage. They asked a few questions but they did not stay long. The Pajaks kept no dogs and they never had done. Mr Pajak disliked dogs and they disliked him, too. It had been noticed in the village that any dog he came near would back away, snarling. In the end one rather fierce dog at a farm was put down. But shortly after that the sheep killings began again.

The girl's death was not the only tragedy about that time. Farmers had started to patrol the roads in cars. That was why Mrs Pajak got killed. The man who ran into her could not afterwards tell a clear story. He had been driving along a twisting upland lane. Coming round a corner, he had seen a huge dog standing there in his headlights, showing its teeth. He had driven straight at it and hit it. Its size had scared him. Surprised and shocked, he did not stop but went on to the nearest house. When he returned with help, there was no sign of a dog. But a woman's dead body was lying at the side of the road. Later it was identified as Mrs Pajak's.

There was an inquest but no one guessed the truth. The man insisted that he had driven at a dog. The jury brought in a verdict of 'Death by misadventure'. Some said that he really had hit a dog. It could have attacked Mrs Pajak just before that and killed her. Her injuries might have been caused by the dog. After the car had hit it, it could have run off somewhere. But they never found the dog or its body. The man, of course, was very upset. He left the district some time afterwards. People tried to console Mr Pajak but they did not get much response from him. He refused all offers of help at the cottage.

His disappearance was not noticed at first. There was too much excitement during those days. The cottage had been rented furnished. When it was found to be empty, all the Pajaks' things had gone. They thought he had simply moved on somewhere else. No one gave the matter much attention. At that time they had had their first real success against the dogs.

They actually managed to shoot one of them. It was not killed outright. There was a full moon but the man with the gun was very excited and his aim was bad. The dog staggered and fell but got up again and ran off. They gave chase and saw what happened. The hillside where they found it was at the edge of a cliff. Below the cliff was a large lake. The cliff overhung the deepest part of this. The dog, with one last effort, dived over the cliff. One or two were even near enough to see the waves from the splash it had made. They did not see it come up again. And there was no more sheep worrying after that.

They will not see the dog again. Some day, perhaps, the body of Pajak will come to the surface. It will have a bullet hole in it. But they will not connect him with the dog. They do not believe in werewolves round here.

It is a terrible fate to be a werewolf. Legend says that a man becomes a werewolf through eating human flesh or through witchcraft. I cannot speak of that. I do not know

71

how it began. All I know is the guilt and terror felt by a person who knows he is a werewolf. It is like a disease that comes over a person when the moon is full.

The Pajaks had moved from country to country. They were always in despair. They always knew what the end would be. Who could help them? Who would believe in the curse that was on them? At the time of the full moon a terrible hunger overcomes a man. Sometimes he can fight against it. I have seen the Pajaks chain themselves on the night of a full moon. I have heard them howl. I have seen them bite at their chains with frothing jaws. But there were other times when they were not strong enough to fight against the madness. The thirst for blood was too strong. Then the wolf shapes would run out silently under the moon. At dawn, they would return in human shape, exhausted, with reddened mouths.

It was a shadow that overhung every moment of their lives. There was no cure and they knew what the end would be. What they faced was certain death at the hands of those whose animals they killed. Animals? Yes—and human beings, too. Why did the Pajaks not kill themselves? I know that they often thought of it.

And how do I know the true story of the Pajaks? At one time, on the nights of terror they would lock me away. That way the son would be safe from his parents. Even later, when they found that the curse had not passed over me, they kept me safe in the house. Now they are gone. After my father was killed, I left the cottage. It will make no difference in the end. But here, in this lonely place, I shall be safe for a little while longer. Maybe, if I keep moving from place to place, I shall live for years. I have the money that my parents left. I can even work by day. I know that when the killing starts, no one will suspect me.

I cannot write any more. The moon is coming up over the hills. It is full tonight. Perhaps tonight, when the madness takes me and I run under that silver light, a bullet will find my heart. But I must go. I cannot help myself. I feel the change coming already.

Even if they shoot a dog and find a man, they will never guess the truth. They will never believe it. Afterwards, whether it happens tonight, after months, after years, someone may find this writing. Will they believe it even then? I can write no more.

My hands are changing. The fingers thicken and curl, the nails becoming claws. It is hard to sit upright. My face is no longer my own. And I must go. The madness drives me. I must go out, under the moon. I must be running, seeking my prey.

Think It Over

What seemed odd about the Pajaks from the first?
What nationality might they have been?
When did they come to the village?
What sort of man was Mr Pajak?
In what way did the killer dogs seem to be clever?
How did the farmers try to defend their sheep?
How often did the attacks happen?
On what night did they happen?
What made the affair much more serious?
What was the reaction of dogs to Mr Pajak?
How did the villagers think that Mrs Pajak might have been killed?
Why did Mr Pajak refuse all offers of help?
What happened to the killer dog after it had been wounded?
What important discovery might be made if Pajak's body is found?
How, according to legend, does a man become a werewolf?
How did the Pajaks fight against the curse that was on them?

What was the only way for the Pajaks to end the curse?
How does the writer know the true story of the Pajaks?
Why can the writer not continue with his story?

Do You Know?

What is sheep worrying? Can farmers kill dogs that worry
    their sheep?
Which kind of people do you like best, talkative ones or
    silent ones? Why?
How old do you have to be before you can own a shot gun?
    What do you need to get before you can buy one? Where
    do you get it?
What is a sixth sense? Do you have one? Do you know
    anyone who has? Describe any experience you have had
    where a sixth sense played part.
How do you know that the raiding animals were at least as
    clever as the farmers on watch?
What might the farmers have realised about the night of the
    full moon?
What is a working dog? What sort of work do Alsatians do?
    What work can Labradors do?
What should you do if you run over a dog in your car? What
    do you do if you run over a cat?
What happens to a body that is drowned?
If you saw an ordinary dog with frothing jaws, what might it
    be a sign of?
Why did the Pajaks lock their son away on the night of the
    full moon?
What does the writer mean when he says, 'It will make no
    difference in the end'?

Using Words

'He returned any greeting quite politely.' What sort of
    words would you use in this kind of greeting? For a
    birthday greeting? At Christmas?

What is the difference between a carcase and a corpse?
What is a culprit?
A *flock* of sheep. Complete these: a —— of cattle, a —— of
   bees, a —— of lions, a —— of geese.
'painlessly destroyed.' Write this in another way.
'the full moon.' What other phases of the moon are there?
Why is a Labrador so called? Why does the word start with a
   capital? How many other animals can you think of which
   are named after a place?
'fierce.' Write down six more 'ie' words.
snarling. How many words can you think of which imitate
   the sound made by an animal?
What is an inquest and how does it differ from a trial?
How many questions can you find in the story? Write them
   out.
'. . . whether it happens tonight, after months, after years,
   someone may find this writing.' Complete the following
   sentences:
   Whether the parcel arrives or not . . .
   He asked me whether . . .
   Whether it makes her happy or unhappy . . .
Use each of these words in sentences of your own: disappearance, success, excitement, actually, happened.

Write Now

In play-form write the discussion some of the farmers may
   have had when they talked about the sheep worrying.
If you had to become an animal which would you choose
   and why?
Write a poem called, 'Full Moon' or 'The Colours of the
   Moors'.
You are a vet. Write your diary.
Draw a picture to illustrate this story or describe the interior
   of the Pajaks' cottage.

75

Haunted

. . . It was a breathy, throaty whisper that seemed to resound through the house . . .

John Marston crushed out his cigarette in the ashtray by the bed and threw his book down. What was the matter with him? He looked out of the window. The last of the evening light was going. After everything had gone so well, he felt uneasy and threatened. Was there thunder in the air?

The house was so quiet. He moved restlessly in the bed and stopped. Pain stirred in his leg. Things might have gone a lot better. If he had not had those drinks—if he had not been driving the car—there would not have been the accident. He would not now be lying here with broken bones. He would have been away from the place.

It was terribly quiet tonight. Perhaps he might have asked Mrs Emmet to stay. No. She would not have stayed. Not after what she had found on that fatal night.

Marston's lip drew back from his teeth in a kind of smile. Things might have been better but they might have been a whole lot worse. Charles might still be alive. Then Marston would not have much to look forward to. As it was, in a week, in a fortnight at most, he would be on a ship on a blue sea under a bright blue sky. Marston's smile broadened. He lit another cigarette and lay back against the pillows. He had a small fortune to spend and no one suspected anything. How could they?

His smile faded suddenly and he sat up. What was that? It had sounded like a footstep. He listened hard. The noise did not come again and he relaxed. It had been nothing. He was quite alone in the house. No one could get in without him hearing it. Mrs Emmet was very careful. She locked all doors and windows before leaving for the night.

There it was again! A soft tread. No—it was nothing. He told himself not to be a fool. He had kept his nerve all the way through. He must not start to crack now. The best thing for him would be sleep. He reached for his bottle of pills. He washed down the dose with a glass of whisky from the almost empty bottle.

Sleep was still a long time in coming. He lay there in the dark and forced himself to ignore the creaks and noises of the house. They were normal. They happen in any house as it cools down after the warmth of the day. Finally, with a sigh of relief, he began to doze.

Soon, he wished he had not taken the pills. He was neither asleep nor awake. His tired mind could not control the thoughts that swam through it. And the thoughts were all about Charles.

When Charles had asked him to come and live with him, Marston at first had been glad. He had lost quite a few jobs. He had had hard luck. He had been poor. He had liked living in Charles's big house, eating Charles's food, spending some of Charles's money. But the pleasure had not lasted long. Charles had got on his nerves. Charles was too quiet. He was too soft. He was too kind in a sickly sort of way.

Marston liked rougher company. He liked men who enjoyed a drink and girls and a game of cards. Of course, there had been some of that down in the village. But Charles had seemed mildly disapproving so Marston had had to stop. After all, he did not want to leave. He had not wanted to lose the luxury of Charles's house and car and money. It was only boring cousin Charles that he could not stand.

Life was very unfair. People like Marston, who knew how to spend money, were poor. Cousin Charles, who did not, was rich. Ideas like that had led to Marston's next step. Murder? Oh, no, nothing like that. Nothing so crude.

Luckily, Charles's health had not been good. Charles worried about it a lot. He had bad headaches. He would try to soothe them by playing the piano. Marston found the piano playing annoying, too. But the headaches and the illness gave him the beginning of a plan.

He had asked Charles if he trusted doctors. Some did not always tell patients the truth. Marston had read a few medical books. Some brain illnesses could not be cured. Some were very painful in their later stages. It had been simple to buy the books and leave them around. He knew that Charles had read them when he saw him become quieter and more worried.

It was not too difficult for Marston to change Charles's medicine. The powder in the capsules was quite harmless. But it did not do Charles any good, either. The headaches got much worse.

One of the signs of the fatal illness was seeing things which were not there. Another sign was hearing voices. Marston could not manage the visions. But he had managed the voices. A tape recorder—a hidden speaker in Charles's room—and finally a time switch. Marston had recorded the voices himself. They woke Charles up at about two in the morning and they whispered advice to him.

'Charles, you are dying. You will die in pain. In agony. It is coming. The doctors cannot stop it. It will tear at your brain like claws, Charles. There is only one way you can escape. You can kill yourself. Charles! You can take your own life!'

There had been different messages at different times. For those last two weeks, Charles had not been quite right in his mind. He had suspected nothing. He had thought that the voices were the product of his own diseased and crumbling brain.

Marston had made sure that he was well out of the way when it happened. He had told Charles he had some business up in London for four or five days. But he had left Charles some messages for those last days. He had to play the game skilfully. The messages had to become more insistent, more frightening. He could not afford to give Charles time to think. Charles must not realise that the doctor had been telling him the truth—there was nothing too serious wrong with him. Charles must believe that he had a fatal and terrible illness. The last message had advised Charles just exactly how he should kill himself.

And it had worked perfectly. Mrs Emmet had discovered Charles's body. She had not yet recovered from the sight. Marston had been able to get the tape recorder from behind the pipes in the attic. He had taken away the hidden speaker. No one had known anything about it. The police had been sorry for him. He had been very upset about his poor cousin. It was the police doctor who had said that Charles must have been mad right at the end. The solicitor had suspected nothing. All Charles's money was to come to Marston. The will had not yet been cleared. But Marston could borrow what he liked.

One thing had not been perfect. And that had been Marston's own fault. He had been drinking down in the village. He said it was to drown his sorrows. Really, he had been celebrating. Coming home, he had crashed the car.

Suddenly Marston was wide awake. He stared at the ceiling, frowning. With the pills and the whisky he should be asleep. He ought not to be reliving the past. He certainly ought not to be open eyed and scared. He made a vow to himself. Tomorrow, broken bones or not, he would get out of this house.

Then he sat bolt upright in bed. What was that? Nothing. It was nothing. Nothing. He shuddered. There it was again. Downstairs. Slow, shuffling footsteps like a blind man feeling his way. That was not the house cooling. Those were footsteps. Marston whimpered.

With a shaking hand he poured his glass half full of whisky and slopped it into his mouth. Some of it ran down his chin and soaked his chest but it steadied him. He listened. There was complete silence below.

Could it have been the branch of a tree brushing against a downstairs window? Had something fallen down there? He drank more whisky and shivered. Those had been footsteps. Someone was in the house with him. He waited.

He imagined the man standing in the hall also listening in the silence. Perhaps he was about to climb the stairs. With the plaster on his leg Marston knew that he could neither run nor defend himself. And it would be no use crawling to the window to shout for help. No one would hear him. It would only attract the intruder below.

Marston stifled a cry. A door down there had opened and closed again. The intruder had gone into one of the rooms, thinking he had not been heard. Now Marston had a chance. He had to get down the stairs to the phone. He had to do it noiselessly and he had to do it now.

He threw back the bedcovers and swung his heavy, plaster-covered leg to the floor. Pain stabbed him like a dagger. But he could not let himself feel pain now. He stood up holding on to the bed. Could he walk? He would have to.

Then, as his full weight came on the smashed leg, it gave under him. He fell with a groan. The shock blazed through his body and his head. When he could think again, he sweated with fear. He waited, expecting to hear the sound of feet running up the stairs. But nothing came. After tense minutes, as it seemed, he began to crawl to the door.

It was the only thing to do. The silence outside was more frightening than any noise. Slowly, inch by inch, he reached the door. He imagined the burglar waiting for him in the corridor. Gently he opened the door. There was no one outside. And the stairs were clear when he reached them.

Biting his lip until the blood came, he eased the agony of his leg down the first steps. Then he froze in horror and surprise. A voice had spoken. It said 'Kill. Kill yourself!' It was a breathy, throaty whisper that seemed to resound through the house.

In an instant he saw it all. It was the police down there. Mrs Emmet must have let them in. They had suspected him all along. They were trying to terrify him into a confession. They were playing back his own tapes at him through some hidden speaker.

He hauled himself back on to the landing and along it. In his half-crazed mind was the hope that he could get to the attic. They had the tape on the recorder up there. He would get the ladder and climb to the attic. He would get the tape and destroy it. That was it! Destroy the evidence. And, all the while the throaty whisper repeated itself, 'Escape . . . take your own life . . . kill yourself . . .'

When he looked up at the door to the attic, he began to sob. He could never climb that flight of steep stairs. But he had to try! Desperately, he began to drag himself up on his elbows. And then he stopped again. The whisper had ceased. He gave a whimper of horror.

Someone downstairs was playing the piano. It was a melody he knew well. He had heard it often enough. Charles had played it many times. The frozen horror that had gripped Marston passed. He let himself tumble back down the attic stairs, not heeding the torture from his leg. He began to scramble along the landing. He could not go downstairs. He dared not face whatever was sitting in the dark down there. He would get into one of the upstairs rooms and out of a window. He did not care what it would cost in pain, now. He had to get away.

A door was open. The bedroom window was a pale square of light beyond it. Moaning, he scuttled in. In the moment he realised that he was in Charles's old room, he realised that he was not alone. A dark shape sat on the bed. There was enough light to see the head and neck.

That dim face had two mouths. One, black against the paleness, was normal above the chin. The other gaped more widely, wet and glittering, in the neck. The chest of the figure was wet and black, too.

'Hello, John,' said the dead, choked voice of Charles. 'I've come back to fetch you.' The words whispered, bubbling and wheezing. Then came the laughter, gurgling and thick.

With a yell, Marston hauled himself to his feet and flung himself away, He was walking, running on his broken leg. His waist crashed into the banisters and he spun headfirst on to the marble floor of the hall below.

Though terribly shocked, Mrs Emmet managed to call the police. The doctor finished his examination of the body and covered it with a sheet. The sergeant, who had been looking at anything but the body, came forward.

'Lived for some time after he fell,' said the doctor. 'He was dead, though, when Mrs Emmet got here.'

'What happened?' asked the sergeant. 'Was he grieving for his cousin?'

'Maybe,' said the doctor. 'He'd been drinking a lot during these last weeks. He was all alone in a locked house. It could have been something to do with imagination—illness. There's one thing I can't understand.'

'What?'

'He was crawling about all over the place before he threw himself down into the hall. There are crumbs of plaster in his bedroom, along the landing and even on the attic stairs. I don't know how long he was at it. With the state his leg was in it must have felt agonising—like a foretaste of hell.' He gave a sign to the two ambulance men and they carried the body out of the house.

Think It Over

What did Marston think was the cause of his uneasiness at first?

How do you know it is late in the day?

Why was he in bed?

Who might he have asked to stay?
What was he looking forward to?
Why did he suddenly sit up in bed?
Why would it have been difficult for someone to enter the
    house?
How do you know that Marston drank a lot of whisky?
Why does a house usually creak at night?
Why had Marston not liked living with Charles?
What was wrong with Charles?
How would Charles try to get rid of his headaches?
How did Marston make these headaches much worse?
What was one of the signs of the fatal illness?
What did the last tape-recorded message tell Charles to do?
What did the police doctor think about Charles's death?
What had spoilt things for Marston?
Why did he get out of bed?
Why could he not escape from the house?
Why did he want to get into the attic?
Who was playing the piano?
How had Charles killed himself?
What was the cause of Marston's death?

Do You Know?

How can you tell when thunder is coming?
When do you first suspect that Marston has done wrong?
Who was Mrs Emmet?
Had Marston committed murder? What do you think?
Why should you not drink alcohol with pills?
When did you last lie awake listening to noises? Where were
    they?
How does a doctor treat a broken leg or arm?
Do people still go on cruises? Where do they go?
How much would 'a small fortune' be today?
Which are the best tape recorders?

What kind of a man do you think Charles really was? Do you take Marston's opinion of him at its face value?

What do you do if you have a headache? What sort of music do you find annoying? What sort of sounds?

What is a solicitor? Why would he come into the story?

Where is the phone in Marston's house?

Why does Marston not try to escape through the front door?

What is marble?

Using Words

What is an attic?

'John Marston crushed out his cigarette...' Write this in another way.

'Marston's lip.' Write about three parts of your head, using your surname and putting the apostrophe in the right place.

Complete the sentences: 'If he had not had those drinks,...' and 'If he had not been driving the car,...'

Use *thoughts, though* and *through* correctly in separate sentences.

'to look forward to' means to antic...

'lost his nerve.' How many expressions can you think of with the word *nerve* in them? There is another in the story. Use them in sentences.

What is the difference between a capsule and a pill?

What two meanings can you think of for the word *record*? Are the two words differently pronounced? How? Which is which?

'not... quite right in his mind.' How many other ways can you think of of saying this?

Use the following words, spelt correctly, in sentences: idea, beginning, quieter, voice, burglar.

Write Now

Make a list of card games or make a list of your relations.

Write a story about a person who begins to hear strange voices which give him orders, or write a story entitled 'Revenge'.

Write an advertisement for a ship's cruise.

Write a poem called 'Ill in Bed' or 'Voices'.

Describe Marston, as if you were Charles.

The Face on the Font

. . . The pig-like eyes seemed to focus on her . . .

She first saw the face on a Sunday morning in church. It was on the font. She had been coming to this church for two months so she was surprised that she had not seen it before. Craftsmen in the Middle Ages had often carved odd designs and faces in parts of churches. Sometimes they did it for fun; at other times they did it for a purpose. But normally a horrid face was outside the church on a gargoyle.

And this face was horrid. It was pig-like with small eyes. The nose definitely looked more like a snout. The mouth had an evil grin to it.

The font was behind her and she found that she kept turning back to look at it. At first her glances were quick and snatched. But as the sermon progressed they became longer. So much so that she became afraid that the vicar might notice her. But there was something in the face that kept making her turn to look at it.

It was definitely the most horrid face she had ever seen. The eyes were tiny and piercing; they seemed to be looking straight into her. The pig nose had very large nostrils. The teeth in the mouth were jagged. Why was such a horrid face on the font?

She normally attended morning service only on a Sunday but she was obsessed by the face all day. It kept coming to her as in a dream. Her mother got cross with her several times for not answering her questions. So much did it obsess her that she found herself walking to the church at evensong. She could not remember setting out for the church: she just found herself entering its lych gate.

This time she sat right at the back so she was on a level

with the font. Yes, there it was, the hideous leering stare. As in the morning her glances kept being drawn to it.

Although it was of stone it had a curiously hairy look. It was yellowy and was cracked down one side which gave the mouth a twisted grin.

Suddenly there was a tap on her shoulder. She jerked round. The vicar was standing over her. The service was ended. Was she all right? She blushed heavily. She said she had been praying and left the church in confusion.

That night she dreamed of the face. It came in and out of her dreams leering down at her from a high place. All the time coming closer and closer. She must have screamed out in the end for her mother was looking over her and tucking her in. She could not tell the dream to her mother. She did not sleep again that night, the face seemed to be hovering over her bed in the darkness.

She had just started work. She was working in an insurance office. She had wanted to give a good impression so for the first few weeks she had arrived at work early. But today she was surprised to find herself getting off the bus at the church. It was as though the face had magnetic power.

She opened the heavy door and went in. The verger was sweeping up. To cover her embarrassment she told him that she thought she had left her gloves there at evensong. Casually she glanced at the font. 'What an ugly face,' she said.

'Yes,' the verger said.

'Why is such an ugly thing on a font?' she asked.

'In the sixteenth century a deformed child was born to a rich man. He had given money for a new font when the child died with strict instructions that it should be made in such a way as it would frighten the devil away from christenings. To do this it was made uglier than the devil himself so they say.'

'It's horrid yet fascinating,' she ventured.

'Oh,' he said and looked at her. 'You find that, do you?'

'Yes.'

'I am a foolish old man and I spend many hours here alone in the church. I must confess that there are many times when I do not feel alone here in the church. I feel its stare following me.'

Suddenly she was bending down to it as if to stroke the face. The verger pulled her back. 'No!' he shouted. 'Do not touch it!'

'Why?' she asked.

'I cannot tell you.'

'Why?' she asked again.

'I cannot,' he said and moved away to another part of the church.

It was too late to go into work now. She would have to say she was sick and have the day off. She wandered round the town gazing into shop windows but seeing nothing. It was as though the face was in a mirror at the back of her mind. She just had to return to the church and touch the face.

This time the verger was not to be seen. She rushed to the font and fell on her knees in front of it. Then she reached out and stroked it tenderly.

It seemed warm for stone and definitely hairy. The pig-like eyes seemed to focus on her and the mouth grin with pleasure. Her heart warmed to it. She bent forward and kissed it. A warmth came through her lips and her face tingled. She leant back with the pleasure of it and gazed on the face. But it was gone.

Her hands were now touching plain stone pillars. The face was no longer on the font!

But her mind now seemed happy and contented. But happy in an evil sort of way. She felt she would love to bend, twist, deform any living thing. A cat wandered in through the door she had left open. She seized it and threw it at the font. It ran screeching away, limping. Her heart was uplifted at the sight and she laughed like a demon. She ran round the church waving her arms.

As she ran by the organ she had a fleeting glimpse of her face in the mirror. What was the matter? She turned and retraced her steps. Oh, horror! The face on the font was on her own shoulders!

Her laughter stopped. There on her own body was the pig-like face. Even the crack was there giving the leering grin. She clawed at her face to remove it. But she felt only solid stone with a hairy texture. She tugged, pulled and clawed at it but it would not come off. She ran back to the font.

The face was still no longer there on the font; just plain stone pillars. She ran back to the mirror again. The stone face on her shoulders was weeping. But they looked like tears of joy.

She ran screaming round the church clawing at her face the whole time. She must find water and try to wash this hideous thing off.

Then she thought of the water in the font. That was holy water. Surely that would wash off this evil thing. She ran there and pushed her face deep into it. She was faint now and her legs were like jelly. She pushed her face to the bottom of the font.

That was how they found her with her arms clasped round the stone pillars. She had died from drowning in a few inches of water.

The coroner said he could not understand it. It was the third case of its kind in the church.

The face is still there on the font. It has its same leering, cracked grin. At times it seems to weep. But you have been warned. If you go in this church, do not look.

But if you must look and are somehow drawn to this face do not touch it. No, above all, do not touch it.

Think It Over

What is a font?

90

How long had the girl been visiting the church?

What surprised her about the face on that Sunday morning?

Where does one normally see horrid stone faces carved on churches?

Why did she keep turning in church?

What was unusual about the fact that she attended evensong?

What was the font built of?

Why did the vicar have to tap her on the shoulder?

How did she spend the night?

Why had she been arriving at work early?

Why did she get off the bus at the church on that particular day?

What reason did she give the verger for being in the church?

Why had the rich man had the ugly face carved on the font?

What strange feelings had the verger had while working in the church?

How did she spend the rest of the day?

What was uppermost in her mind?

Why did she return and touch the face?

What happened when she kissed it?

Why did she turn back to look again in the mirror of the church organ?

Why did she use the water in the font?

How many times had strange deaths occurred in the church?

Do You Know?

When were the Middle Ages?

Name two kinds of modern craftsmen.

What is a sermon?

Why might the face have had a piggish look? Is there anything about a pig which seems horrible? What?

What is evensong?

How many services are there in your local church on a Sunday?

How old is the girl in the story? What evidence can you give for your answer?

What sort of work does a verger do?

Why might the girl have wanted to stroke the face?

What made her hurt the cat?

Why does a church organist need a mirror?

How do you feel when you are faint?

Had she killed herself? What had killed her?

Using Words

Write sentences of your own using each of these words: font, aisle, pews, altar.

snout. What other words are there for 'nose' including slang words?

What animals do you find ugly? Make a list.

What animals do you find beautiful? Make a list.

'So much did it obsess her that she found herself walking to the church at evensong.' Complete the following sentences:

So pleasantly did they spend the afternoon that . . .

So urgently was the medicine required that . . .

So marvellously did the performance go that . . .

Use each of these words in a sentence of your own: sometimes, curiously, suddenly, embarrassment, definitely.

Use *threw* and *through* correctly in sentences of your own.

Use *whole* and *hole* correctly in sentences of your own.

leering grin. What sort of expression does a leering face have? Explain in your own words.

'she had a fleeting glimpse.' Write this in another way.
What is the difference between 'a day off' and 'a day out'?
Can you think of any other expressions that use the word
   day?

Write Now

In play-form write the conversation that the craftsman who
   carved the face might have had with a friend or his wife
   about it.
Describe how someone might feel on their way to their first
   day at work.
How many churches are there in your area? Can you list
   them or draw a map?
Write a poem called 'Watched'.
Write a story about black magic in a church.
In play-form write the conversation the verger might have
   had with his wife after he found the body.

M'Bula

. . . Its teeth gleamed and its skinny arms writhed as it capered there . . .

I have never seen a man so changed. I had never liked him. But when we met him at the airport, I was sorry for him. He was thin-cheeked, his clothes hung on him, and the sun seemed to have turned his skin more yellow than brown.

He talked brightly enough. He talked too brightly. He seemed half-crazy with relief, either at seeing us or being back in England. But he talked about anything but Africa. On previous occasions he had always been full of himself and his war experiences.

He was my wife's cousin. His name was Graham Burns. He always stayed with us because he had no other family. He called himself a soldier. What he really was, was a mercenary. He would be off to fight in some war somewhere and he would return to us full of boasting and swagger.

There was none of that when he returned this last time. In one thing, though, he did run true to form. He never had brought presents for the children and he didn't bring any now.

We got him settled in at home and tried to get used to him. It was harder than it had ever been before. He got on Mary's nerves a bit. I was out at work all day. She said that he used to prowl round the house or stand for what seemed hours just looking out of the front room window. He seemed as jumpy as a cat. I did get him to go out one night. We went to the local pub. But we didn't stay long.

Two Jamaicans came in. He simply rushed out. I had to follow him. It wasn't prejudice. He was just terrified. He stood there under the street lamp and he was trembling. We had to go home.

We had his nightmares to put up with, too. They didn't happen every night but they happened often enough. After the worst one we got him to see a doctor. The sleeping tablets helped after that.

But the nightmare scared me. A nightmare? It was more than that. His calling out in the night had scared the children. I'd got into the habit of sleeping with one ear open so that I could go in immediately and wake him. That night he was more talking than shouting. I got up and went into his bedroom. It was dark in there but I could see he was out of bed.

He stood in the middle of the floor.

'I wasn't in charge, M'Bula,' he panted. 'It was Giles who ordered it. Giles. Not me. But he's dead. That's why you're doing it to me, isn't it? But I didn't give the order. Get away! Keep away!'

I had started to shake him by the shoulder as soon as I went in. He didn't seem to feel it. He went on talking. Then he pushed both hands out in front of him like claws. Those last words were a scream. I was scared, too. I had both hands on him, shaking him as hard as I could. Then he shuddered and groaned. I put the light on. He looked round as if he didn't know where he was. I saw utter relief spread across his face.

'Dreaming again,' he mumbled.

'You certainly were,' I told him.

'Talking, too?'

'Yes.'

'What about?'

'Somebody called M'Bula. And orders. Look, Graham,' I said, 'what's this all about? What happened in Africa?'

'Nothing,' he said. 'Forget it. It's a bit of fever I brought back. It gives me these bad dreams.'

He got back into bed. He tried to light a cigarette but couldn't. His hands were trembling too much. But that was all he would say about it, then or afterwards.

Both Mary and I tried to get him to talk about it. What had he done in Africa that was making him like this? But whenever we started, however we went about it, he shut up like a clam. If we pressed him, he turned savage. He'd stamp off up to his room and get stuck into his whisky. He still had enough nerve to go round to the off-licence for a new bottle when the old one ran out.

He got more than savage in the end. I'd just come home one night. I was putting the car away. Then I heard Graham yelling like a madman in the house and Mary yelling back. I ran in. As soon as he saw me, he started on me.

'Those kids! Those damned kids!' he began, grabbing me by the arm. 'What have you been saying to them? What have you told them about me?'

'What kids, for God's sake? Get hold of yourself, Graham!' I told him. It did no good. He ranted on.

'Your kids! Out there in the garden! Jeering! Laughing! Calling my name! They've got other kids with them. They've blacked up all their faces and lit a bonfire.'

'The kids are out at Dawson's party tonight,' I told him. 'They haven't been near this house since they left for school this morning.'

'They're out there now!' he raged. He went over to the French windows and pulled the curtains back. 'I was up in the bedroom—' He stopped. The lawn outside was bathed in winter moonlight. And it was totally empty. It was utterly quiet.

So was he—then. The silence seemed to drag on for minutes.

'They weren't English children,' he whispered at last. 'They were those in the village. Those flames—' His voice broke off. 'M'Bula,' he said. It was more like a groan. He went straight up to his room.

Mary and I decided to leave him alone. We thought we'd talk to him about it in the morning. He would have slept off whatever was bothering him by then. That's what we thought. But it didn't turn out like that.

It must have been about two in the morning. I woke up and lay there wondering what the noise was. I realised I had heard someone go downstairs. Then the screeching began. It made my blood run cold. It was coming from the front room. I had cold shudders running down my back as I went downstairs. It was almost reassuring to find out what it was.

I'd worked out by then what had wakened me up. It was the sound of drumming.

Our eldest lad, Martin, has a bit of a drum set in the front room. He had a drum set, I should say. It wasn't a toy. It was a real drum, a what-d'you-call-it, a snare drum on a stand. He has the cymbal that went with it still in there.

But I knew before I opened the front room door that I wasn't hearing a snare drum. It was much deeper in sound. The rhythm was strange, too. African. It resounded through the house. But when I opened the door and switched on the light, that seemed less important than what I saw.

Graham had stopped screeching. He was snarling now and crying at the same time. He had a carving knife from the kitchen in his hand. He had slashed the skin of the snare drum to ribbons.

'Graham!' I said. I had to call his name a couple of times before he stopped and turned to look at me. And the pounding drum ceased abruptly.

Somehow I got him back into bed. He was babbling all the way. He kept talking about Giles and petrol and getting them all into a hut. He said something about trying to get information by threatening the kids. And the name M'Bula kept coming up time after time in all the babble. I got two sleeping tablets down him and sat by him until he went off. Just before he fell asleep he said that people had to do some pretty lousy things in a war. Then he thanked me and seemed to go out like a light.

He was different again in the morning. We suggested that he see a doctor. He told us to shut our traps. We insisted that he needed treatment. He said that he was the best judge of that and we should leave him alone. I was pretty fed up with the whole thing. I asked him straight out.

'What happened in that village, Graham?' I said. 'And who is M'Bula?'

'You shut your damned mouth about that!' he snarled. 'I'm the only one who knows anything about it. All the rest are dead—even that old swine, M'Bula. So—shut your mouth!' And he went out slamming the door behind him. It was not long after that that we heard the front door slam, too. When we looked upstairs, we found that he'd taken all his things with him.

He didn't seem to be safe, off by himself like that, poor devil. But we couldn't decide what to do. We thought of going to the police at first but what could we have said to them? He hadn't done wrong. He was a grown man. He'd gone off of his own accord. Still, it worried us a lot. I still feel very guilty about it now that it's all over.

That morning, though, I felt relieved when Mary rang me at the office. She'd found out by chance where he had gone. He wasn't far away. He'd booked himself a room at a small hotel just at the edge of town. Mary and I talked it over when I got home that night. We felt that we ought to talk to him again. Mary didn't want to leave the children on their own. So I drove over by myself.

When I got there I sat outside in the car for what seemed like a long time. But I went in at last. By then, they'd got Graham's door open and the hellish business was all over.

They'd heard him shouting, pleading and finally screaming before all noise had stopped. But they hadn't been able to get in to him soon enough. His door had been jammed. They had had to break it down. And it had been too late.

He wasn't even badly burned. It couldn't have been much of a fire, though they did say that the crackling of the flames had sounded fierce through the door. Graham's window was clearly visible from where I had parked in the street but I had seen no flames. He was dead all the same. A tragic accident. No one could have saved him. I couldn't.

As I said, I sat outside in the car for a while. I was forced to, you might say. It wasn't just the drum, though that was paralysing enough. It was the same deep tone I had heard in our house. A strange, alien rhythm, ferocious and triumphant. It seemed to go on for hours, though I couldn't have been there for more than about a minute. No. It wasn't just the drum.

There was a little patch of grass to the side of the hotel. It was clearly lit by the light from a street lamp. I saw the figure there clearly before it disappeared. It was an old man, black as ebony, bare-legged and bare-chested. It wore a crown of waving ostrich plumes on its bony head and a loin-cloth of leopard skin. Its teeth gleamed and its skinny arms writhed as it capered there. It was dancing. A dance of joy to the eerie music of the drum.

Think It Over

Why was the writer sorry for Graham Burns when he saw him?

Where had Burns come from?

What was his job?

Why did Burns get on Mary's nerves?

Why did he rush out of the pub?

What else upset the family at night?

Who was Burns talking to in his nightmare?

How did the writer finally make Burns wake up?

What happened when they tried to get Burns to talk about Africa?

How did Burns pass the time?

What made the writer run into the house when he returned from work one night?

What had made Burns angry?

What did he see when he drew back the curtains at the French windows?

What woke the writer after that, during the night?

What kind of drum was making the sound that resounded through the house?

How did the writer get Burns off to sleep?

Why did Burns eventually leave the house?

Why did the writer and his wife not go to the police?

Where had Burns gone? How did they find out?

Why did the writer not go into the hotel at once?

Why was the drum triumphant?

Do You Know?

Where is your nearest airport?

In what way had Graham Burns's personality changed?

What is the difference between a mercenary and a soldier?

How do you know that Burns was not a generous man?

Where is Jamaica? Can you name two other islands near it?

What is the fever that men can catch abroad from mosquitoes?

Who had been the leader of the mercenaries?

Name two things African tribes use drums for.

What other thing besides the heat kills people in fires?

What is the best thing to do, if your house catches fire and you are upstairs?

What is the difference between a snare drum and a bass drum? What is a cymbal?

What do you think Burns had done to the African children?

Who is M'Bula?

Using Words

'full of boasting and swagger.' What is *swagger*?

'true to form.' Where does the phrase come from? What does it mean?

'mercen*ary*.' How many other words do you know which end -*ary*?

'prejud*ice*.' How many words do you know which end -*ice*?

'prowl.' What other words can you think of which describe the way an animal moves?

'mumbled.' Another word which shows that a person speaks with difficulty is sta . . .

'It made my blood run cold.' What other ways are there of saying this?

List all the hyphenated words in the story.

'He told us to shut our traps.' What would be a politer way of saying this?

Use each of these words in a sentence making sure that the spellings are correct: soldier, occasions, immediately, relief, quiet.

What sort of things are ferocious?

Write Now

Write about some war experience as though you had been there.

Make a list of all present day African countries.

In play-form, write the conversation between the story-teller and his wife, Mary, when he gets back from the hotel.

Describe, as if you were one of the villagers, what happened in the African village.

You are the manager of a hotel. Describe some of the strange guests who stay there.

Write a poem called 'The Thing That Followed Me' or 'The Drum'.

Tundra

Those huge arms enclosed him in their dark embrace. . . .

The wind moaned undyingly across the dead wastes of the tundra. The land stretched away, flat as far as the eye could see. Wilson had been moving steadily across it all day. Ten days before a helicopter had dropped him and Matthews with a fortnight's supplies. Two weeks should finish the surveying work they had to do for the oil company.

It was not dangerous, Wilson thought. But the place got to you in the end. It seemed to bite down into the very marrow of your bones. The wind howled and the frozen land rolled away on all sides. It waited and it threatened.

He snorted, impatient with himself. He had been feeling vaguely uneasy all day. It was not the cold or the wind. He had got used to those. The land was empty. It was all in his imagination. There had just been a bit too much of that last night.

He and Matthews had stayed up late, talking. Like two children, Wilson thought irritably, scaring themselves with tales of the dark. Matthews had been among Eskimos. He had talked of the spirits they believed in. There was Sedna, Mother of the Sea Animals. She was so horrible to look at that only the most wise and cunning of medicine men could see her and live. There was Kigatilik. Anyone at all who came across him fell prey to his power and his huge fangs. They had talked of the Wendigo, the spirit of the forests. No one had ever seen him. Yet the sense of his presence was so terrible that men were forced to run from it until they died.

Wilson shook himself free of such thoughts. He would be better off setting his mind on his work. There was nearly an hour of daylight left. He looked round, frowning. But what had happened to Matthews? He had been there not a moment ago. And not more than a hundred yards away.

'Matthews!' he yelled. 'Jim! Where have you got to?' Only the wind made any kind of an answer. 'Jim!' He began to hurry towards where he had seen Matthews last.

He reached the place and hunted around. There was no marshy pool into which Matthews might had stumbled. There was no hollow in the ground which might be hiding him. 'Jim! Jim Matthews!' he called over and over again. The whine of the wind mocked him.

At last the uneasiness he had been feeling all day rose in a wave and broke over him. All round him was the tundra, mysterious and deserted. Utterly empty. There was no place Matthews could have gone.

He had better get back to camp. Matthews had gone missing. God knew how. The best thing was to get back to camp and report over the radio. Suddenly the thought of speaking to another human being seemed the thing he wanted most in the world. He hurried.

And then he found himself running. He could not stop himself. Nor did he want to look behind. He had been wrong about the daylight. Dusk was coming quickly and bringing a mist with it. His imagination peopled the empty tundra behind him with weird shapes. The breath was sobbing in his lungs when he came at last in sight of the camp. The relief he felt was wonderful.

It was not just the sight of the tent and the thought of the radio. Matthews was back at the camp. His figure squatted just outside the tent. He had probably gone back to prepare supper. Maybe he had called out when he had set off back. Wilson just had not heard his shout.

Wilson stopped with his head down and his hands on his knees to get his breath. He stood up and waved. The familiar figure in its fur hat and striped jacket waved back. Wilson went slowly on, keeping his eyes on the rough ground underfoot. It wasn't all that rough but he was a bit ashamed to meet Jim Matthews' stare. He betted that Jim had seen him running like a scared kid across the tundra.

He looked up when he got close to find that Matthews had disappeared again. He hesitated and then went on, calling out. 'Jim! Have you got the tea brewing? I hope you've got the stew on.'

He had reached the tent when Matthews came into sight round the side of it. Just for an instant, the figure seemed to be Matthews. Then it changed, horribly.

It was not Matthews. It was not even human. Neither was it like any beast that Wilson had ever seen before.

Wilson had no time to scream. Those huge arms enclosed him in their dark embrace. The monster jaws closed upon his head.

Then, in a short while, the land was quite empty of men once more. The mindless wind tugged and battered at the sides of the tent without pause as the night came on. There was no longer any black and monstrous figure to be seen. But the savage spirits of that land dreamed and waited.

Think It Over

What is tundra?

How long had Wilson been out on the tundra that day?

How long had he and Matthews been away from their base?
How many days had they to go before they were picked up?

Who were they working for?

What had Wilson and Matthews been talking about the night before?

Name one of the evil spirits that Matthews had mentioned. What did it look like?

What time of day was it when the story begins?

Why was Matthews' disappearance strange?

Why was Wilson pleased at the thought of using the radio?

Why did he run back to camp?

What made him feel relieved when he got there?

Why did he walk up to the camp with his eyes on the ground?

What happened to him?

What was the only thing left in the landscape as the night came on?

Do You Know?

What sort of people use helicopters and for what purpose?

What is the marrow of a bone?

Have you ever been scared, telling tales in the dark? What happened?

What would be the most frightening thing for you about the tundra?

What might have happened to Matthews?

What is the flattest country you know?

In what country might this story take place?

Where is the coldest place you have ever been?

Have you ever been aware of complete silence all round you? Where were you and how did it feel?

What sort of sea animals would Sedna be mother of?

Name some European monsters of legend.

What does the fact that the pools were marshy in that region tell you about the season of the year?

How would they have powered the radio out on the tundra?

What sort of clothes would they need to wear? Why would they have needed hot meals? How might they have heated their tent?

Using Words

'The wind moaned . . .' Can you think of three other words

which would describe the blowing of the wind? There are others in the story.

American Indians called this person a 'medicine man'. African tribesmen would call him a 'wit . . .'

'*oil*' Make a list of words with -*oi*- in them.

'Have you got the tea brewing?' How do you ask this question in your house?

'their dark embrace . . .' Use *their* correctly in three sentences of your own.

'She was horrible to look at. Only the most wise and cunning of medicine men could see her and live.' Join these two sentences without using *and*; then compare your version with the one in the story.

Use these words in sentences of your own, making sure that their spellings are correct: dangerous, irritably, medicine, uneasiness, wonderful.

Write Now

Describe the monster that Wilson saw, or draw your own illustration to the story.

You are completely alone on a desert island. Describe how you spend your day.

Find out what you can about Eskimos and write a short article about them.

What do the oil company men find when they land in a helicopter? Write out their report.

List the things you should do when camping in a lonely place and the things you should not.

Write a story about being out in a high wind or a gale.